Turning

Stories about Choice and Change

Featuring:

- Ruth Boggs • William Cass •
- Julie Carrick Dalton • PJ Devlin •
- Brandon French • Wendy Fontaine •
- Ted Harrison • Joani Peacock •
- Barrington Smith-Seetachitt • Kelli Sullivan •
- Thelma Zirkelbach •

To: Lee
I love you.
Dad 2017

Edited by Meredith Maslich

Possibilities Publishing Company

ISBN: 978-1-947486-03-4

Published and distributed
by Possibilities Publishing Company

www.PossibilitiesPublishingCompany.com

Table of Contents

Editors' Note

The theme for our 2017 Anthology contest: *Turning Points: Stories about Choice and Change,* was absolutely inspired by all of the changes in the world's current political and social climate. We live in a time when, more so than ever before, the choices we make as individuals can have global impact. The 2016 Presidential election was a major turning point for this country and the larger global community as well, as things that many had viewed as certainties — reproductive choice, residency, health care, identity — changed almost overnight.

However, the theme is also a nod to the fact that change is what makes a story, a story. Change is the magic ingredient that takes an anecdote, or series of observations, or sequence of scenes, and turns it into a riveting, memorable, and relatable narrative. Change provides shape, tension, and emotional resonance to a story through it's universality. No one is immune to change. It is thrust upon us by forces seen and unseen, when we seek it and when we don't.

When selecting the pieces for this anthology we looked for stories, both fiction and nonfiction, that explored the idea of turning points in different settings, contexts and narrative styles to provide as wide a perspective on this theme as possible. I feel like we've accomplished that goal and I hope you'll agree.

Change, as the saying goes, is really the only constant in the world. So let's explore it together through art, and try to find insight, inspiration, empathy, or even just some distraction and entertainment, as we naviage our own turning points.

—*Meredith Maslich, CEO*
Possibilities Publishing Company

Quinton Parnell Arrives in Ocracoke

Ted Harrison

"Quinton, we went this way before!" Laura Jean was my girlfriend, but she could pout at times, times like this. I purely hated that.

"You think I don't know that?" My old '97 Lincoln Town Car was running good, and it was a nice day, but I hated it when she told me what I already knew. All the car windows were down so we could get a breeze, and then she threw some beer cans out of the window. "What did you do that for?" I wanted a place to use my surfboard. All she wanted to do was lie out on the beach and get a tan, drinking beer in the process. The island of Ocracoke, North Carolina might fill both 'wants.'

"Because they were empty, silly." She popped open two more cans, handing one to me. "Lord, I bet there ain't two thousand people in this Ocracoke place. What kind of damn name is Ocracoke? I would not want to live here. That place we were last night, that Hatrack or something like that, it was okay. But here?" She leaned to look out all the windows. "Seriously?" Slurping her beer showed she was getting a buzz. Then she burped, sounding like a fifty year old man. Of course, her blue bikini made sure I knew the difference.

"A lot of this island is a national seashore park. Federal land." I thought about telling her that some people might think our hometown, Valdosta had a funny name. Thought about it, but kept quiet. I don't poke sticks at hornet nests, either. Like a lot of other beaches some of the buildings here perched on stilts to avoid high water. One bar had very steep stairs I'd hate to climb—up or down.

"Guess that's because nobody else would live here. I was hoping for some game arcades. Roller coaster rides. Nothing like that here." Now, she was whining. I liked what I had seen. I mean Ocracoke was hot, hotter than I'd had figured for mid-April. Hot and humid, so maybe that caused Laura Jean to ball up some plastic bags and more empty cans then fling it all out the window, too.

"Laura Jean!"

"What? I bet they have people here who can pick up trash just like in real beach places." She eased her feet up on the dashboard; it was a little awkward because she had cut one foot on a seashell at Hatteras. "When can we go to the beach? At least find some awesome rides." She started playing with the hair on my neck. "It was nice up at Hatteras." She could pronounce the word when she wanted to. She was being spoiled. "More to do. I liked the shops there." She tried to tickle my neck. "Please, Quinton."

"Oh sure. So you could complain about me watching movies, and I could complain about no waves. Seriously?" She leaned close to me, rubbing her breasts on my arm.

"Well, if you wouldn't watch all the old, oldie movies. Ohmygod! Some of the movies were in black and white. Black! And! White!" Like each word was a sentence as she punched my arm.

We had been on the island about an hour, just taking our time. It is an out of the way place, minus a lot of the plastic crap you can find in some touristy places—places like Laura Jean wanted to see. No need to go back toward Hatteras. This street looped around some sort of bay that looked like a lake, about the size of two or three football fields. The street ran around three sides of the lake. When I looked to drive down another street I thought I saw a police car about a block behind us pull out to follow along.

Even after a single beer, I didn't need to attract police attention. Laura Jean started guzzling beer on the ferry from Hatteras and was still going strong. "Don't look now, but I think there is a police car following us." I should have saved my breath. Laura Jean dropped her feet down, squirmed around in her seat so she could do the opposite of what I said.

"Who is it? Barney Fife?" She giggled. "Where's Sheriff Andy? We are in North Carolina." Finding a couple more empty cans, she tossed them out the window, too.

"Laura Jean!" I started laughing myself. "Gomer will be along soon, I'll bet." Turning onto Highway 12, I sped up, but not much.

"Woohoo!" she yelled. "Roll on, Quinton." She beat on my arm with her hands like I was some sort of drum.

In the rear view mirror it looked like the police car had slowed down. We were already out of the village. Up ahead there was a little unpaved road that looked like it led to the beach. We wound around little sand dunes where I figured to hide. "Keep an eye out! See if he comes after us." Still leaning over her seat into the back of the car, she was fumbling in her gym bag and peeking out the back window.

We stopped behind a little mound of sand—not big enough to call it a dune—and waited. All the while I was huffing and puffing. You would have thought I'd been running, not driving. Besides, I was close to pissing in my pants.

"I think we ducked him," she was still looking behind us. I eased the car ahead about ten feet when she squealed. "Damnit!"

The police car was between us and the beach. "If we get to the ferry, we still don't know when it leaves!" I slammed my hand on the steering wheel, and saw Laura Jean leaning out the window on her side of the car. POW! "What the hell did you do, woman?"

She laughed and held up a little pistol. "I slowed him up."

She was right about that. The police car swerved in the sand and stopped. Panicked, I gunned the Lincoln. POW! "Damn it! Do NOT shoot that gun again!" Driving less than a hundred feet, we skidded in the sand, jamming my car door. Sand was level with the car window on my side. "Crap!" Next smoke poured from under the hood.

"Quintonnnnnnnnnn! What happened?"

"Shut up, Laura Jean! Just shut up!"

"Don't you talk to me like that!" She hit me using the same hand that held the gun.

"Oh hell!" Blood began dripping from my nose.

Laura Jean clapped her hands to her face, dropping the gun on the seat. "Oh, baby! I'm sorry. I'm so sorry." She reached for me, but I was climbing out my window. Pulling my shirt up to wipe at my nose, I began to get my balance and started running toward the highway. Laura Jean would have to handle this herself. I could hear the police car revving up. I figured the officer was trying to get unstuck.

"Quinton! Honey! Come back! I'm sorry!" I could hear Laura Jean yelling. "Quinton Parnell! You sorry bastard! Don't you leave me here!" There was a moment of quiet, then, "Officer! Go shoot him! You hear me! He left me here alone." She sounded like she was crying.

I got to the highway, crossed over it and pushed into the tangle of trees and brambles. I just had to get away. The car was mine. What they might find in the trunk wasn't really mine, but they wouldn't care. They'd open up the trunk and find two pounds of pot there, courtesy of Laura Jean's sorry-assed brother, I figured. He had been working on the Lincoln. I wasn't smart to let him do that, but he was a good mechanic. Still it was in my car. Sure, I could tell the law that I didn't know how it got there. If somebody tried to tell me that I'd say, "Bullshit"! Laura Jean didn't know about the pot. She could be very persuasive, so maybe she could make cops believe it. Maybe I was the most nervous explorer ever to arrive on Ocracoke.

Needing to get to the Sound, I tried to run in the tangled mess, until I stepped in a hole and fell! Spitting sand out of my mouth gave me time to think a little bit more. When Laura Jean and I made love the first time, all we had was wine. She said she only use alcohol. Lying there remembering, I could tell my nose had stopped bleeding, but a couple of new long scratches trailed down one arm. With an ankle burning and my back aching, I didn't expect to hear voices, but I did.

"How big of a water sample do you want me to get?" A kid, I figured.

"Just get about half a jar full." This from an adult male. "Anybody think there might be clams here?"

Several voices, each with different opinions, clamored to be heard.

"It's usually easier to find them in tidal flats. The mud. North Carolina Sounds have some tidal effect…"

"I found one, but he ain't in the mud." I looked up through the branches of a little tree to see a boy; about ten years old. "He's in the bushes."

"How do you know it's a 'he', Justin?" The man was closer now.

"I saw him, just before I was about to take a whiz." Sure enough, I could see now that the kid had unzipped his pants.

The man came closer. I couldn't see his face because the sun was behind him, but he looked very tall. "Well, and who do we have here in the wonderful wilderness of Wokokon?"

"Huh?" That was all I could muster. I could see the kid roll his eyes.

"Wokokon. It's another name for Ocracoke." The man moved enough for me to gather in his features: slim, sun blond hair hanging to his shoulders, wrinkled face peering at me, his eyes shaded by a well-worn visor that might have been red a long time ago. He reached to help me to my feet. "Dalton Krider. I teach science at the school." His gray shirt may have been black a long time ago; likewise, the jeans he wore rolled up to his knees.

By now about a half dozen other kids had joined us. The first boy came up from behind me. I guessed he had found friendly ground to relieve himself. "Hi, guys." I smiled.

"You look a little the worse for wear," Krider said. His smile didn't reflect warmth. He looked at the children crowding around. They all looked about the same age as the first kid. Each of them had a jar or plastic container. "Well, we're getting water samples from the Sound for class."

That was when I looked out across the water. All I could see was more water. On the ferry ride I hadn't paid much attention to the inlet we crossed. Laura Jean was in a playful mood at that time. "I was trying to get to a little creek along here. Looking for a boat I heard was for sale." I still smiled, but as far as this crowd I seemed to be more like some creature that belonged under their microscopes.

"Can we go now? I want to get to the lab," one little girl piped up.

Krider swept his hands at the children to herd them along the shore away from where we stood. A couple of the group cast looks over their shoulders our way. "I don't know about any boats for sale, but there is a little creek that empties into the Sound up that way." He pointed away from the direction the children went. "Maybe you'll find what you're looking for. Maybe fifty yards along." He lifted his visor and re-set it on his head. "Great place Wokokon." This time his smile was real.

"Okay, thanks." I turned and limped along the shore line.

Warm water from the Sound served to wash my face and remove the blood from my arms, before heading the way he had pointed. More water felt good, but tasted like licking an ashtray. There was a smell to the place. Not bad, but not a fragrance like flowers. Tangy, like smelling the game ball just before the Friday night kickoff. Inhaling made me want to breathe it all inside.

Three little boats were anchored near the mouth of little creek. One of them might have been white once upon a time. It was nearly submerged. Neither of the others was from this year's market. The one that looked to be the older was tied to a tree by an old rope. It was easy to push out into the Sound, but a little harder to be aboard.

The next part was not easy. For the next five minutes I tried to get the ancient outboard motor started. I tried to prime it. There was a little bit of gas in the tank at the bottom of the boat, but motor wouldn't turn over. Where could I go if the motor wouldn't crank? It seemed like time to figure out if I was going to go and face the police. Try to bust Laura Jean out of jail? Facing the music meant owning up to the dealer quantity marijuana in my car. With the unhappy realization that I had no idea what to do, I slipped back into the water and walked the boat back into the creek.

"Hey. Need help?" A man yelled, but then laughed because his shout made me slip on the muddy Sound bottom. I fell, but didn't go under water. Two men were in a small boat about fifty feet from shore. Both looked old enough to be my grandfather's father. Their boat had an outboard, but they used an electric trolling motor, so I hadn't heard them approach. One wore a faded red shirt with long sleeves, buttoned to the neck, and his head was covered by a wide brim hat, which seemed more suitable for farming than fishing. The other man's sweat shirt was only meant to accommodate today's weather because the sleeves had been scissored off just short of the shoulder seam. His long white hair was stuffed through the back of his Atlanta Braves baseball cap.

"No. Thanks, though." I was almost back to where I could tie up the boat when a siren wailed. The sound came from back up the creek, likely on the road. The rope to the boat slipped in my hand.

"What the hell's that?" The one in the wide brim hat craned his head. "Sounds like a car on the road."

"Who the hell knows? It was a lot quieter back when we didn't have a police department." The other laughed.

"Well. We'll be going. You might need to check the plugs." Wide hat nodded a farewell. They moved slowly and quietly away. The creek bank invited me to take a rest.

The sirens echoed away from the village, toward the Hatteras ferry landing. It seemed time to reconsider. Walking hurt my ankle, but seemed to help my back. I wandered along the shoreline back toward the village of Ocracoke. I had a little bit of knowledge about this island. You could take a boat, the ferry or an airplane to get there. Well, I knew I couldn't swim away. Now that I was here, getting away involved the some three methods. Without an airplane, boat or ferry, I was stuck. In summary, I had no plan. And no prospects.

The sun continued to drop toward the horizon as I went the way I had come through the tangled weave of trees and undergrowth. Back at the road it was time to take stock. To the left I could try to walk the miles to the ferry to Hatteras toward the noise of the sirens. To my right I could go back into the village. I was tired. Weary. Beat down. Any close to the ocean, I might have waded out into the waves. My feet directed me to the right.

Just on the edge of the village two cars headed my way, so I got off the road. Near a house clothes were hanging out to dry. A stupid phrase came to mind: 'clothes make the man.' With a pair of overalls and a short sleeve shirt from the line, I scrambled into the bushes to change. The shirt and overalls were too big, but that didn't matter. I still had a little cash. I wound my old clothes up in a heap, and I scraped sandy soil to cover them. I was still cautious when I got back on the road to continue my walk.

Finally, I saw something familiar—my old Lincoln, but with yellow crime scene tape staked around it. The car was sitting in the parking lot beside a convenience store just on the edge of the village. One lone customer stood pumping gas into his pickup truck, paying as little attention to my car as he did to me.

Inside a woman in green shorts and a dark blue t-shirt was placing a loaf of bread and a six pack of beer on the checkout counter. "And how much gas did he say he was going to get?" She spoke to the clerk who looked a little older than me, maybe thirty, dark hair and beard, wearing a red vest with BUY QUIK embroidered on the pocket. The woman looked at the man at the gas pump. "The old fool said he needed thirty dollars' worth. So make sure he don't go over. I'm paying for this with my money. He's going up to work on the ferry. If he wants to fill it up, he can do that when he gets paid. Ain't that right?" She chuckled. "I sure will be glad when the tourists get here. It has been slow at the café." She laid bills on the counter and the clerk made change. "See you. Have a blessed day." It sounded as if she meant it.

I was thirsty. The bottle of water from the cooler went down in three swallows. Limping along the aisles I could see was a store that had everything from axe handles to vitamin pills.

"First aid stuff is two aisles to your right."

The clerk's voice surprised me. "Huh?"

"I saw you had some bad scratches. We've got some antiseptic cream and bandages."

The second bottle of water tasted even better than the first. In the meat case several slices of bologna rested at the butt end of a large round. My mouth watered. "Can you sell me a couple of slices of bologna?" Food seemed more important than any first aid. From what I could tell by one of those big overhead I didn't look as bad as I felt. Right now bologna and the Lincoln held my thoughts.

"Sure." The clerk came back, slipping on plastic gloves. "Two? More?"

"Two's plenty." I pulled the cash from my pocket. He wrapped the meat in butcher paper and taped it, then peeling off the gloves, he went back to the front of the store. On another aisle I found a package of saltine cracker and a little jar of mustard and put it on the counter.

The clerk was totaling the cost, and I could see that I was going to be short. I moved the mustard out of counting range, then I had twenty seven cents to spare. Helluva fix. Can't even buy mustard

"Here." He reached under the counter and pulled out a plastic squeeze bottle of mustard. "I used to have some of those little packages, but lately I use this." He pushed the mustard toward me.

"Mighty nice of you. You like it around here?"

"Oh yeah." He looked out the window. "Ocracoke is one of those places where folks can leave you alone. But it's small. Folks can know what you've done before you do." He chuckled, looking satisfied with himself. I stood holding my bologna and crackers, and he began straightening the stock near the checkout.

"What's the story on the old Lincoln?" The grimy window, all but covered with advertising signs, allowed only an abbreviated view of the car. A breeze stirred the yellow tape. My surfboard was off the roof rack and propped against a front fender.

"Police had it towed here earlier. Something about a drug dealer trying to escape or something."

"Drug dealer?"

"Yeah, well I don't know about that. Thing of it is, the local officer said he was chasing this car that went into the National Seashore. He said somebody in the car shot at him, then he got stuck in the sand and the other car—that car out there—got stuck, too."

With some mustard on the bologna folded in between a couple of crackers I could grunt, but that was all. He wanted to talk. I wanted to listen.

"Ocracoke doesn't have an impound yard, so the wrecker used our parking lot."

"Did they arrest anybody?

"They got a girl. There was a man and a girl in the car... Nobody knows where the man went. 'Course I don't believe he'll get far. Office Gaskins said 'Ocracoke is on lockdown.'"

"Damn!" I know my mouth dropped, and I shook my head. "Drug dealer. Huh!" The tight feeling in my gut didn't come from hunger.

"Well that's what Gaskins said, but he's the only one who said that. After the car was dropped off, he came here and searched it up and down. I watched him. Couple of other customers saw it, too. Gaskins came in and got a soda. He was mad because he didn't find any drugs."

By now I had finished the bologna, with a few crackers and most of the second bottle of water left over. "So what about the woman?"

"Arrested her. Of course there is a little bit of a squawk about the whole thing."

"Charged her for being a drug dealer?

"Somebody said she had a little derringer pistol and shot at Gaskins. I don't know that for sure. And I don't start gossip. But I can tell you, there's no drugs in that car." He put out his cigarette to greet the man and woman entering the store. "Evenin, ya'll"

Outside I sat on the bench eating the last of the crackers. It was a good place to think about what the guy had said about no drugs. What time I wasn't looking down at the ground, I was looking at the car. I figured I had seen the last of that car and the surfboard. Chalk the whole thing up to being a part of life. I didn't care a damn thing about the pot.

A few more people came and went to the store. I must have sat there over a half hour, long enough for my ankle to feel better and still enough to make my back hurt again. I quit looking at the car, tried to quit thinking about the drugs. I had done wrong leaving Laura Jean. Shadows elbowed away the light as the sun went down leaving my old car in the dark. Moments later nature lost the game when several large fixtures threw light over the parking lot. My old Lincoln was a forlorn product of the process. It was time. I started walking.

Family Recipe

Wendy Fontaine

I know the moment when my four-year-old daughter falls asleep. Lying in bed next to her, one arm draped over her bare shoulders, I wait for those slow seconds of surrender, when her eyelids grow heavy, little by little, until they eventually slip down like old window shades. Her mouth slackens into a tiny pink parenthesis and her body, so full of energy during the day that I wonder if her veins pump liquid electricity, slowly releases into the stillness of slumber.

But on this night, surrender doesn't come, and I see in the glow of the moonlight through our bedroom window that Angie is still awake. She stares across the room, past her purple desk and her shelf of teddy bears, toward something I cannot quite make out. A wrinkle tugs at the skin between her blue eyes.

"Mama?" she whispers into the dim light between us. "I have a question about Grampa."

"Yes, honey?"

I expect her to ask when my father might die. It's a question that all children ask eventually, first as curious little ones and later, differently, as adults. When will our parents die, and what will life be like without them? It's something I ask myself whenever I see my father fall asleep on the couch after lunch or hold his glasses up to the sunlight to check for smudges.

Angie rolls onto her back, revealing the creamy outline of a nose, cheeks and chin that curve like my own. She smells like me, breathes like me. She asks her questions, so many questions, just like me.

"Well," she says, turning her face toward mine. The moonlight drapes over her furrowed brow. "Is Grampa ever nice to you?"

Her question is another that I have considered over the years, although only briefly because that answer, too, is slippery. The answer must be yes. Yes, of course there have been times when my father was nice to me. When I was a kid, he took me to see Santa Claus. Whenever he stopped at the corner store to buy beer, he gave me spare change to buy a few handfuls of penny candy. On windy days, he walked my brother, Brian, and me to the football field behind our house to fly kites. Many of those times began with good intentions but, for one reason or another, deteriorated into arguments and hurt feelings. Now, as an adult, as a mother, I see how easily that can happen, how swiftly a moment can sour.

When I was ten years old, my father took us fishing every Sunday afternoon at Schoolhouse Pond. Brian was five then. We stood at the shoreline, watching the waves lap at the grassy banks instead of paying attention to our red plastic bobbers.

"Watch your bobbers," Dad grumbled, pointing to the tiny red tomatoes bouncing in the choppy waves. "When it goes underwater, you have a fish."

He opened the wicker fishing basket, optimistically wide for all the bass we were going to catch. Maybe we'd snag a perch or a pickerel too. But after a few minutes, our tomatoes began to drift and blend in with the watery reflection of trees and clouds and daydreams. The rocking motion of the waves lured us toward droopy states of inattentiveness, a kind of hypnotic mood that could only be broken by the fear that Dad would notice our forgotten tomatoes before we did. So Brian and I tugged our poles, hoping that we had caught something for the wicker basket. Instead, our lines twisted in the weeds.

I dreaded the moments when anger overtook my father. It transformed him, huffed and puffed inside of him, until it finally took control. It yanked the poles clean out of our hands and ransacked the tackle box, looking for new bobbers to replace the ones that were tangled, never to be retrieved.

My daughter could not have known the sound of her grandfather's fury echoing over Schoolhouse Pond. Or could she? Could she know how Brian and I endured those summer afternoons, how quickly our excitement turned into fear?

In my family, we celebrate with lasagna. There's no recipe, not one that has ever been written down anyway. We simply remember it. A palmful of Parmesan. A sprinkle of oregano. A pound of ground beef and some curly-edged egg noodles. And through it all, inside every layer, a thick red tomato sauce.

It was my grandmother Angelina's recipe, or at least I have always imagined that it was hers, handed down to my father and then to my mother after they were married. At some point, perhaps as soon as I was tall enough to see over the kitchen counter, it was handed down to me, and I will pass it along to Angie someday.

One snowy day in February, I decided to make lasagna for my family. Angie and I were visiting my parents' house in Maine from our home in California. We were all together, and I wanted to mark the rarity of this occasion with food, as most Italian families do. As Angie played Go Fish with Grandma in the living room, I whirled through the kitchen preparing ingredients.

"Grandma, do you have any sevens?" my daughter asked. She sat with her legs folded under her on the old rocking chair in the living room, next to the china cabinet that my parents bought before I was born. When I was in fifth grade, my brother threw a toy fire truck at me during a fight. I ducked, and the fire truck sailed like a comet through the glass door of the cabinet. My parents left the glass broken. For years, I thought they just never got around to fixing it. Later on, I wondered if leaving it broken had been intentional, a solemn reminder to all of us about the destructive power of anger.

While Angie and my mother traded cards, I mixed the cheese with pepper and egg, then browned beef with garlic and onion. Tomato sauce bubbled like lava on the stove.

Outside the kitchen window, my father plowed the driveway. He had been out there for hours, and nothing, not even the smell of simmering sauce, could lure him inside. Finding things to do always came easier to him than finding things to say. When we were kids, Brian and I figured he was just in a bad mood, and so we steered clear of him. After I was grown, with a child of my own, I wondered if it were something more, if maybe losing his mother left him at a loss for how to be a parent, or if the sight of lasagna ingredients spread across the kitchen counter reminded him of her. Either way, he spent the afternoon outside, plowing snow and puttering around the yard. When the snow finally let up, he came inside and stood in the doorway like a bear roused from hibernation.

"Move your car," he hollered, his salt-and-pepper beard full of snow. "I need to finish the driveway."

I looked down at my hands, covered in tomato sauce. It was almost dinner time, and I had two more layers to prepare before the lasagna would be ready for the oven.

"I'll be right there," I told him. "I'm almost done."

"No, move your car right now." His words were cold and defiant, with the measured tone of a challenge and the low rumble of far-off thunder.

My father had yelled at me many times during my adolescence. When I listened to his Paul Simon records while he was at work. When I forgot to turn off the bathroom light. When I brought the car home on empty. And every time, after every fight, I escaped to my bedroom, where I cried until my eyes were swollen. But this time was different. My daughter was in the next room. Already, hints of temper were beginning to show in her tiny acts of resistance, which were cute at such a tender age but would only grow bitter with time, given her family's bloodline. I wanted my family legacy to be lasagna, not hostility and rage, so I held my father's gaze, letting the red sauce drip from my fingertips.

"What the hell are you looking at?" he asked.

"You shouldn't talk to me like that," I said.

"This is my house," he said. "I'll talk to you any way I want."

I felt a familiar heat deep inside my body, felt it rise and burn like a flame. I stomped out of the kitchen to the bedroom, yanked our empty suitcase from beneath the bed, and ransacked the closet in a blaze of balled-up socks and twisted pajama bottoms. I wanted to escape, to get as far as possible from my father's meanness, as though breaking away from a family history of anger could ever be as simple as packing a bag.

I know the moment when my daughter is about to lose control. Her face reddens, as though all the blood in her body has been summoned there. She squints to hold it all in but it builds inside of her, growing hotter more quickly than I can temper it. Then finally, it spills out, through her mouth, through her eyes, through her breath.

"I hate you! You're the worst mama ever!"

On a Friday afternoon at the city swimming pool, Angie's anger blew like a bottled-up volcano. Her eruption left a crowd of mothers with mouths agape, frozen in mid gesture, like mummified victims of Mt. Vesuvius. She wanted to stay at the pool to keep swimming, but it was time to go home and start dinner.

"We can come back another day," I told her.

"I wish I'd never been born!" she yelled. "I hate you!"

She flew at me with both arms, landing slippery punches on my elbows, then raking her fingernails down my forearms. She kicked at my ankles and screamed over and over again.

"That's it," I said. "You're in trouble."

I yanked her by the hand toward the parking lot as the other mothers watched, their faces locked in expressions of horror. Angie pulled herself away from me. "No!" she said. "I'm not leaving!"

She looked me in the eye with defiance that boiled over. Then she drew in a deep breath and spit at me, her bubbly white saliva clinging to my hot skin. As her spit slid down my arm, the swimming pool faded away. The crowd of mothers disappeared. There was only me, frustrated and flush, and my daughter, indignant and determined.

Sometimes I wonder where the anger will take me. Will it spin around inside itself, swirling and churning until it tires of its own irascible energy? Or will it make me do things and say things I can never take back? Will it send me down a path from which there is no redemption?

Before I could think to stop myself, my hand flew from my body like my brother's airborne Matchbox car. It landed on Angie's face with a fiery slap, shocking us both into silence. She didn't scream or cry. She stood frozen and stunned, her mouth and eyes wide open. I froze too, with shame and disgust. I felt small and mean, like a bully. I scooped my daughter up, cradled her body in my arms, and kissed the tomato that was forming on her cheek.

The mark faded, but the guilt I felt for hitting her remained. And my hand, my hand would be red forever.

In my father's living room, the hypnotic glow of the television screen fell upon my daughter's milky white forehead. I slipped her arms into the sleeves of her blue fleece jacket and slid her winter hat over her crown of brown hair, never once pulling her attention away from the flicker of cartoons.

Outside, I started the rental car and turned on the heater. Maybe we could get a hotel, I thought. Fly home early. With a plastic snow scraper, I chiseled the ice that had formed on the car windshield. Layers of thick, stubborn ice.

"Are we going to talk about this?" My father had followed me to the driveway.

"There's nothing to say," I told him. "You can't talk to me like that in front of Angie."

"If you leave now, then you can't come back," he said.

I saw the hurt in his brown eyes.

"That's fine," I said, looking away.

I didn't want him to see the hurt in mine.

In those moments, I wonder what the anger will do. Will it be a barricade between me and my family? Will it live inside me, turn me into the parent I never wanted to be? Or will it be a constant admonition, a stern but silent reminder of how many people it can hurt?

I left him in the snowy driveway and went back inside to hug my mother goodbye. She gave me an extra squeeze, the kind that silently apologizes. I lifted Angie and carried her outside, where my father stood between me and the car.

"You need to think about the way you talk to your family," I said. "They are scared of you. But I don't have to be. Not anymore."

My father stood silent, in scuffed work boots and oil-stained jeans, looking smaller than ever before. In that moment, it wasn't his anger that scared me. It was his frailty.

"I talk the way I talk," he said, shrugging.

"Yeah, well, it's hurting your family," I said, pushing past him to get Angie into the backseat. "Has anyone ever talked like that to you? Do you know what that feels like?"

He didn't answer. He didn't need to. I already knew that my father understood, perhaps better than any of us, what it felt like to be scared of someone.

When I was a kid, I heard stories about my grandfather. I listened to my aunts and uncles when they thought I wasn't paying attention. In one story, my grandfather threw a knife at my teenaged father during an argument. When my father ducked, the knife sailed over his head and pierced the tree behind him. They said my grandfather had beaten my grandmother, Angelina, many times, including once with a dog chain in the backyard. My father had tried to stop him, but couldn't. She died from a blood clot in her brain, on Valentine's Day, when my dad was 22. No one ever told me her death was caused by the beatings. That was an assumption I made as a child, listening to conversations I wasn't supposed to hear.

I met my grandfather once, at a cousin's birthday party when I was nine. He sat in a green tweed chair in the living room, leaning forward like he had something important to say. When he talked, his breath smelled like booze. He seemed too small, too feeble, to have been the angry man in those stories. But even then I knew how anger could change a person. It could come on like a storm when you thought the sky was clear.

In the driveway, I stared at my father, not with spite or animosity, but with sympathy. His stubbornness slowly dissolved into shame. Some people are better parents than others, but not one of us is perfect. We all have moments of regret and disgrace. We want to surrender them, to release and forget the hurt we've caused, but instead we struggle beneath the weight of them. Our worst mistakes are the heaviest and hardest to bear.

"I can try harder," my father said. A tear slipped below his glasses. One layer, melting away. "Sometimes I don't know what I'm saying."

There are moments like this when I forgive, partly because I don't want to argue but also because I'm hopeful. I want to believe that we are all capable of being better. My father can be kinder, and I can be a more patient mother. While some moments can never be reclaimed, reversed or unraveled, others, if we are willing to face them with honesty and humility, can begin to repair the ones that have hurt us.

That afternoon at the pool, I wiped Angie's saliva off my wrist. I led her by the elbow toward the car, where I buckled her into her booster seat. Before I closed the car door, she grabbed my arm and kissed the spot where her spit had landed.

At my parents' house in Maine, I hugged my father. He felt like a little bird in my grasp. Afterward, we dragged the suitcase back inside and finished the last two layers of lasagna. Angie and I woke the next morning, ready to head back to California on schedule, and I said goodbye to my father in the driveway, which had once again filled with snow.

"I'll try harder," he said, for the second time in two days.

"I hope so," I told him.

It might take years, maybe even generations, to replace our anger with compassion. Every day, I make my own unspoken promises to my daughter, not to be perfect but to be fair and calm, to listen instead of yell, to hug instead of hit. In each of these moments, I promise to try harder, for her and for the daughter she might have one day.

Angie and I lie in the moonlight, our arms and legs tangling under the cool surface of the bedspread. I feel her muscles relax and hear her breath fall into the gentle, rhythmic pattern of far-off ocean waves. I lie there listening, thinking about how much my dad must miss his mother, how sad he is every Valentine's Day, how everything around him is a reminder of her life and her death. It's in the food he eats. It's in the name of his first-born grandchild. It's in his blood.

"Is Grampa ever nice to you?" my daughter asks again. Her eyelids softly slip down. I kiss her brown hair.

"Yes," I whisper. Her head falls heavy into the curve of my collarbone. Her pink lips fall apart and her body, finally, lets go.

This essay appeared in Tiferet Journal in Fall 2015 and won the journal's Tiferet Prize for creative nonfiction.

The Spirit Walk

Ruth Boggs

Sixty miles north of Caspar, in the Big Horn basin of the Red Wall backcountry of Wyoming, Willow Creek Ranch stretches across 57,000 acres and is home to the "Hole in the Wall" of Butch Cassidy and the Sundance Kid fame. Remnants of their cabins still linger under Cottonwood trees, with Buffalo Creek rolling by only a few feet away.

There are few distractions here other than breathtaking scenery, hardworking cowboys, and three squares a day. No cell phone reception, no Internet, and no T.V.

I'm one of ten writers who've come for a weeklong writing workshop hosted by authors Janet Hubbard and Tina Welling. We sleep in log cabins, eat in the bunkhouse at the chime of the triangle, workshop and write, and we take excursions to explore the ranch and let the solitude and magnificence of the vast prairie landscape inspire our creativity. Tonight, our schedule reads "Spirit Walk."

In her book "Writing Wild," Tina Welling describes a Spirit Walk as employing the three parts of the brain – reptile, midbrain, and neocortex – for a three-step process of consciously experiencing nature by naming, describing, and interacting.

Notebooks and pencils in hand, we set out to do just that. In three four-wheel drive vehicles with battered windshields, which all trucks on the ranch seem to have in common, we are driven to a plateau a few hundred feet below the rim of a gigantic Red Wall.

The trip, through rugged terrain and up a steep hill, is not for the fainthearted, but the bumpy ride is worth it. The panorama offers a breathtaking view of the fading sun tinting the endless sky in a multitude of blood orange hues.

"I want you to go off on your own and consciously experience your spirit walk", Tina instructs us. "Take lots of notes. Take your time. We'll meet here again after the sun has set."

As we head off in different directions, one of the drivers cautions, almost casually, "Be careful, though. There are rattlesnakes up here."

The words stop me cold in my tracks. I'm terrified of snakes. I can handle bugs, spiders, or rodents, but snakes conjure up a primordial fear in me unlike any other creature.

"It's okay," the driver says, sensing my fear. "You just have to react appropriately."

"What do I do if I encounter a rattlesnake?" I stammer.

"You keep quiet and back away very slowly."

Most likely, I'll do exactly the opposite. I'll probably let out a bloodcurdling scream and run as fast as my legs will carry me.

Timmy and Suzi, two fellow writers, are already heading up the hill. Janet and a few others are off in search of the magical meditation spot she found on her last visit here, and the rest are also spreading out.

I'm the only one still standing there, apprehensive, frozen and immobilized by fear.

Suddenly I feel woefully unprepared for this adventure. Most of the others are wearing cowboy boots or hiking shoes. I'm wearing open-heeled sneakers and no socks. That's as good an excuse as any not to venture into rattlesnake territory.

The way from the plateau to the rim is a tangle of sagebrush, coarse gravel, rocks and boulders, and patches of bright blue lupine and other sturdy mountain flowers. A rattlesnake would be visible in spots barren of vegetation, but getting all the way to the rim also means wading through dense, knee-high shrubbery and ground cover.

I look up the mountain and the struggle inside me intensifies. I don't have to do this. I have an excuse: I'm not wearing the proper footwear. But I know that's just an excuse. What holds me back is fear. Fear of rattlesnakes or all snakes in general. I know it's a fifty-fifty proposition: maybe I'll encounter a snake, and maybe I won't. It all boils down to whether I'm willing to take the risk.

My rational brain tells me that I don't have to do anything I don't want to do. It's completely my choice. I can simply say no and leave it at that, opting to go downhill and explore the grassland instead. But my emotional brain tells me that I'm going to regret not going all the way to the top.

Other situations come to mind, when I was also crippled by fear and took a risk. Afterwards, I was always glad I did. In Costa Rica, I didn't want to go snorkeling because I was afraid of triggering a persistent medical condition. But then curiosity triumphed over fear. I went for it, first slowly venturing forward clutching the hand of a local diving guide, and later going out into the coral reef on my own.

Floating through huge schools of exotic fish was pure exhilaration. I sustained some scratches on the sharp coral, but I also saw Dory. Yes, Dory. There is indeed a deep blue fish, and I would not have seen it if I hadn't been willing to venture out of my comfort zone. The hour I spent snorkeling turned out to be the absolute highlight of my two-week Costa Rican adventure.

All this crosses my mind as I scan the obstacle in front of me: a steep hill dotted with clumps of sagebrush and wild rosemary ground cover that possibly harbors rattlesnakes.

My reptile brain and my neocortex are at odds. The former makes my heart beat faster and my body stiffen up in fear, while the latter beckons that this moment in time is unique. It will never come again. Not in the same way. I will regret it later on if I don't take advantage of it.

Time is of the essence because the sun is sinking fast. We have to head back down the mountain before it gets dark. I need to make up my mind now. Soon it will be too late and then hesitation is bound to turn into regret.

It is that sentiment that prompts me to slowly, almost mechanically, put one foot in front of the other and venture up the hill. My eyes are fixed firmly on the ground as long as I'm in rocky terrain. But halfway to the rim, I can no longer see much of the ground I'm walking on. The shrubbery gets denser as I advance, caressing my calves and obscuring my view of the ground.

I pause and take some notes about the shapes, colors, and textures of the shrubs and rocks that cover the ground. I smell the wild sage that finds purchase on this barren soil. I notice whitewashed bones of animal carcasses, gnawed clean by vultures and other predators and bleached by the sun – but no rattlesnakes.

I'm tempted to stop right here. I've already filled my notebook with plenty of notes about the endless wide-open spaces, sloping hills and magnificent rock formations, the deer and antelope dashing across grasslands, the colorful sinking sun, the sensual sound of gravel crunching under my feet, the noise of howling wind, mooing cows and chirping birds, the smell of fresh air, and the fragrance of wild sage. I even tasted the sage; its bitter taste is still lingering on my tongue. Why not stop here?

But the magic of the moment, the holiness of this vista, the overwhelming view, draws me forward. I can sense that there's more. I want to go up all the way,

I want to experience all of it, I don't want any regrets later on. I want to make it to the top, to the rim. And I do.

When I get there, I stand motionless, taking it all in. I carefully avoid looking downward. The 90 degree drop is several hundred feet. One wrong step here, and I'm done. But my inner voice is not done with me yet. There's more. I can't just come here, look around, and leave. This begs to be my place to meditate and let my spirit soar.

I turn around, and with my back to the rim, slowly get on my knees. On all fours, I inch backwards until my feet are no longer on solid ground. Then I turn over, sit down, and finally let my legs dangle over the edge in a perfect 90 degree angle spooning the rim.

I sit motionless, eyes closed, arms outstretched, palms up, and face raised to the sky. I inhale deeply and feel the cool breeze on my face and the stillness of the waning day. I hear the soft howling of the wind and subtle sounds of the deer and antelope. As I listen more intently, even the quietness has its own sound.

When I open my eyes again a good while later, the sun has set behind me. The Red Wall casts a large shadow over the vista, and the wind is cooler than before. A delicate band of silver mist rises from the grasslands, signaling that nightfall is approaching rapidly.

I don't want this moment and this utterly peaceful feeling to end, but it must. We have to make it down the mountain before dark. Supporting myself with both hands, I carefully slide backward, eventually turning over on all fours again to get up. For a split second, a quick series of 'what if's' goes through my mind and makes my pulse beat faster.

But nothing of the kind happens. I don't misstep. I make it away from the edge without slipping. My cell phone does not fall out of my shirt pocket and bounce down the mountain as I roll over to get up. And I've not once thought about rattlesnakes during the time I sat here.

Going down the mountain, I feel unburdened, enlightened, relieved, victorious, and a bit giddy.

The exhilarating feeling that I've just accomplished something big buoys every step I take on the way back. Unburdened by the fear I left up at the brink, my spirit soars as I almost skip down the mountain. I feel like I've just conquered the world.

Just Like That

William Cass

Nick's wife, Afsanah, was a nurse and had the day off, so they decided to go for a picnic with their four-year-old daughter, Laya. It was a Wednesday, and the small park along the bay they went to was practically empty. Nick pushed Laya on the playground swings while Afsanah spread a combination of Iranian and American food across a blanket on the grass nearby. Then they sat in the shade of a tall eucalyptus tree and ate, watching the boats on the bay and the occasional passerby on the walkway.

An old man passed them walking a dog with brilliant white, bushy fur as Afsanah was putting things away in the basket after they'd finished. The dog stopped to sniff at them, and Laya knelt up and reached her hand out tentatively to touch its side.

"Go ahead," the old man told her. "He won't hurt you. He's very gentle."

Laya stood and moved her hand more boldly, scratching the dog between his ears. As she did, the dog turned his head and licked her hand. Laya looked up suddenly at the old man. He smiled down at her, then at Nick and Afsanah, and they smiled back. The dog stood perfectly still as Laya moved her hand through the thick fur along his back.

"He's beautiful," Afsanah said,

The old man nodded with satisfaction. "He's a show dog. We just got back from a regional competition. He won third place."

"Wow," Nick said. "How about that, Laya?"

She grinned and nodded.

"Well," the old man said, "we'd better be on our way."

Laya stepped back, and they watched the pair move off down the walkway. The old man was short and dressed all in white: white tennis shoes, white socks, white pants, and a white windbreaker zipped to the chin of a deeply tanned and wrinkled face. He shuffled slightly as he walked. They watched the dog tug him a little onto the grass, where the old man stepped into a depression surrounding a sprinkler head, turned his right ankle, gave a little yelp, and fell on his side.

Afsanah reached him first and kneeled beside him. He grimaced and reached his hand toward the ankle he'd twisted. The dog licked once at his face.

"I'm a nurse," Afsanah told him. "Let me look at your ankle."

He watched her as she gently lifted his ankle onto her lap and felt around it. Nick and Laya came over and stood a few feet away watching, too. The old man winced as her fingers probed the outside of his foot. The swelling there was evident under the white sock.

"I'm afraid you've sprained it," Afsanah said. "Not badly. You don't need to go to a hospital or see a doctor, but you do have to ice and elevate it as quickly as possible. How did you get here?"

Through clenched teeth, he hissed, "Drove."

"Where's your car?

"Over there." The old man cocked his head towards the row of diagonal parking spaces across the grass at the curb. "The silver Caddy."

They all looked at the car he indicated, which was parked just a few spaces from their own.

"Do you live close by?'

He turned slightly and winced again. "Couple miles."

"All right," Afsanah said. "Well, you can't drive yourself with that ankle, so I'll bring you home in our car, and Nick can follow in yours. Nick, help me get him standing."

They did. The old man draped his arm around Afsanah's shoulder and she supported him as he limped gingerly across the grass. The dog walked by his side with the leash dangling behind him. Nick gathered their picnic things, and they hurried ahead. At their sedan, he opened the passenger side door for the old man and the back door behind it for the dog. He and Afsanah helped the old man into the seat. Before Nick closed the door, the old man reached into his pants' pocket and gave his keys to Nick. He looked back and forth between the two of them and said, "Thanks."

The dog hopped up into the back, whining a little, and Nick closed that door, too. Afsanah arranged Layla in her booster seat on the other side of the dog, climbed in behind the wheel, and backed away. Nick got into the old man's big car, set the picnic basket and folded the blanket on top of a pile of papers on the passenger seat, and followed closely behind.

Afsaneh drove slowly so Nick wouldn't lose sight of her. They passed their own section of town with its apartment buildings and crowded bungalows and entered an older, established neighborhood of wide tree-lined streets and large estate-like homes. Afsaneh turned into a long driveway and stopped in front of a two-story home with columns and a fountain near its double-doors. Nick pulled in beside her, and they both turned off their engines.

As Nick lifted the picnic basket and blanket, he upset some of the papers on the passenger seat that fell onto the floormat. He set the picnic items on the driveway next to his open door and reached for the papers; by the recent dates and notations at the bottom of each, he saw that they were all printouts from various Internet web sites. The headline of one had to do with the need to limit immigration to the U.S. from Middle Eastern countries. Another was about a southern state's legislation to hold U.S. sponsors of Middle Eastern immigrants liable for any crimes they committed. The last was an online petition in support of the travel ban to the U.S. for some largely Muslim nations; words were scrawled in uneven handwriting on top that said, "Find out how to sign this".

Nick's eyebrows knit and he blinked at the papers he held, a chill crawling over him. He thought of how he met Afsaneh early in college after she'd come from Iran on a student visa; she was a couple of years ahead of him in school. Nick watched her help the old man out of the car and thought of the extra shifts she put in at the hospital so he could stay home with Laya and work on his master's thesis. He watched his daughter with her sandy-colored hair like his and his wife's dark complexion smiling and rubbing the dog's fur from her booster seat, and shook his head. The water from the fountain gurgled quietly. He placed the papers where they'd been on the seat, shook his head again, got out of the car, and carried the picnic items over to the sedan.

Nick handed Afsaneh the old man's keys as they passed him and unfastened Laya from her booster seat. He lifted her out of the car and the dog came behind her. Nick put the picnic items on the seat where the dog had been and followed them himself.

When he entered the house, Afsaneh already had the old man lying on his back on a couch in his big living room and was arranging throw pillows under his injured ankle. She unlaced his shoe on that foot, removed it carefully, and went into the kitchen. The old man held the back of one hand over his eyes and groaned. Grass stains stood out on the knees of his white pants. The dog nosed at the old man, then curled up on the floor next to him. Laya settled herself in a chair at the antique desk in the corner, took a sheet of paper from the computer printer beneath it, lifted a marker from a cup, and began to draw, humming as she did. Nick remained just inside the doorway and surveyed the room with its ornate

furnishings and large gold-framed mirror over the fireplace. When his eyes fell
on the old man, he felt his stare harden and his jaw clench.

A few moments later, Afsaneh returned to the room with a bag of frozen
corn and a dish towel. She knelt at the foot of the couch, fitted the bag around
the injured ankle where the swelling was most pronounced, and tied the towel
loosely around it.

"Leave that on your ankle for as long as you can," she told the old man, "and
keep your foot elevated like that. There's another bag of vegetables in the freezer
you can rotate to when this one thaws, but don't move any more than necessary,
and keep your weight off of that foot when you do."

The old man had removed his hand from over his eyes. He nodded.

Afsaneh looked towards the darkened interior of the house and asked, "Is
there anyone here to help you?"

The old man shook his head. "My wife is dead. We had no children."

"All right. Well, the sprain isn't too bad, so you should be okay in a day or
two. Just limit your movements and keep the ice on and the foot elevated, even
when you go to bed tonight."

"My bedroom is upstairs," he said. "But I'll sleep right here." He gestured
with his hand. "Can you hand me those afghans?"

Afsaneh took the two afghans off the high-backed chairs next to the couch
along with one of the throw pillows on them. She lifted the old man's head and
arranged the pillow under it, then spread the afghans over him.

He fingered the fabric, looked at her, and said, "My wife made these."

"They're lovely."

He nodded.

"Do you want a glass of water or something before we go?"

"No, I'm fine. I'm grateful for your help. I'd still be lying there on the grass if
it wasn't for you."

Nick thought about the papers in the old man's car. "Come on, Laya," he
said. It came out hard. "We're leaving."

Afsaneh gave him a puzzled look as Laya hopped down from the chair and
brought the paper she'd been drawing on over to the old man. She held it out to
him and said, "Here, I made you a picture. It's you and your dog."

The old man took it from her and studied it, nodding, a small smile creasing
his lips. He set it on his chest, looked at her, and said, "Thank you."

She bent down, rubbed the dog's fur, then took Afsaneh's hand.

"So, you'll do what I've told you?" Afsaneh asked.

"I will, yes."

"All right, then."

They turned and came toward Nick. The old man didn't return his stare. But his wife glared at him as she and Laya passed him. He closed the door firmly behind them.

The three of them drove home in silence except for Laya's humming. They went into their ground floor apartment through the back door that led into the kitchen. Laya continued into the living room where Nick and Afsaneh heard the television turn on. They put away the picnic items in tandem without speaking until Afsaneh finally said, "What was that all about?"

Nick closed the refrigerator door, turned, and faced her. He pursed his lips looking at her.

"Well?" she said.

"He had anti-Muslim rhetoric in his car." Nick spoke slowly and as evenly as he could. "News articles about curbing Middle Eastern immigration here and a petition supporting the travel ban."

His wife's expression didn't change, but she folded her arms across her chest. A long moment passed. Finally, she said quietly, "I see." She opened a cupboard and began placing picnic items in it. Nick watched the back of her. After another moment, she said, "That doesn't change the fact that he needed our help."

The next morning, Afsaneh rose early while Nick and Laya were still sleeping. She changed quietly into her nursing uniform and then busied herself in the kitchen. Nick silenced the alarm next to their bed when it woke him an hour or so later, dressed, and got Laya ready for preschool. When they came into the kitchen, Afsaneh had cereal, bowls, spoons, milk, glasses, and orange juice on the table. There was also an aroma of saffron in the air and a sealed Tupperware container on the counter.

"Good morning," Afsaneh said. They watched her gather her purse and pull on her jacket from a peg near the back door. "I have to catch my bus. Breakfast stuff is ready." She looked at Nick. "And I've made some Khoresh to heat up for dinner. It's in the fridge. There's also some in that container for the old man from yesterday. I want you to bring it to him after you drop Laya off at school and check on him. Ask him to show you his ankle and be sure the swelling has gone down. See if he needs anything."

Slowly, he shook his head. He said, "You can't be serious."

"I am." She leaned forward and kissed his cheek and then Laya's. She said, "Have a good day."

Nick was still shaking his head after the door closed behind her.

The old man's car was where he'd left it the day before when Nick came up the long driveway a little later. He parked in the same spot as the previous day, turned off the engine, and sat listening to it tick. He looked out across the manicured grounds, the stands of tall, well-maintained shrubs that separated the old man's property from his neighbors on both sides, and the murmuring fountain. Hummingbirds hovered at a feeder dangling from one of the porch eaves. Nick blew out a breath, lifted the Tupperware container off the seat next to him, and walked to the front doors.

He heard shuffling from the living room inside after he rang the bell, and it took several minutes before one of the doors opened and the old man appeared in its cavity, the dog at his side. He was dressed exactly as he'd been the day before, but his clothes were rumpled and his hair was mussed. He looked as if he'd just awakened, but recognition soon filled his face. He dropped one hand on top of the dog's head and said, "Hello."

"My wife asked me to check on you," Nick said. "See if the swelling on your ankle has gone down."

The old man nodded and slowly extended the leg he'd injured. His pants slid up exposing the ankle; the swelling there was almost gone.

"See," the old man said. "Better. Thanks to your wife and you."

"Mostly her."

The old man cocked his head and made little shrug. Over his shoulder, Nick could see the tangle of afghans on the couch and the drawing Laya had made taped over the antique desk. It dangled alone there on the wall.

He extended the Tupperware container, still warm, and said, "This is for you, from my wife."

The old man frowned, then his eyes widened. He took it in both hands. "Smells wonderful."

"It's Koresh, an Iranian stew. It's good."

The old man looked from the container to Nick. Their eyes held. The old man said, "Please thank her for me."

"I will. Is there anything else you need?"

"No." He shook his head. "I'm fine."

Nick nodded and walked back to the driveway. When he passed the old man's car, he glanced in the passenger side window. There were no papers on the seat. He stopped, squinted, turned, and saw the old man watching him.

"There were papers on your passenger seat yesterday," Nick said. "Articles, those sorts of things. They're gone now."

"I threw them away," the old man said. "I don't want them anymore."

"Just like that."

"Yes." The old man paused. "Just like that."

They regarded each other while the dog whined quietly and nosed at the old man's leg. Nick turned towards the street and shook his head.

"Maybe your daughter can come over sometime to see my dog," the old man said. "Visit. Laya."

Nick looked back to him. He said, "I'll ask her."

Then he got in his car and backed out of the long driveway. As he turned onto the street, he looked back at the house. The old man was still standing in the open doorway; he raised one hand from the container he held and showed its palm. Nick did the same before driving away.

On Slickrock

Julie Carrick Dalton

Evening sun skimmed the canyon rim, casting a rusty iridescence across the cliffs. Tara's lungs burned as gravel churned between the slickrock and the treads on her mountain bike.

"I would love to have seen Burns' face," her son Peter shouted over his shoulder from his bike. He was almost as tall as Tara now.

"It felt pretty awesome." Thinking about Chester Burns, the Utah State agriculture professor, made Tara's face hot. "He's got to accept that the days of grazing on federal land here are ending."

Hours earlier she had stood in a claustrophobic room defending her doctoral thesis, stating that it will take the desert one hundred years to recover from damage caused by cattle on public lands.

"Burns was so condescending. 'You're talking to a fourth generation cattle rancher, young lady,'" she mimicked Burns' drawl. "He said that in front of the whole panel. 'Young lady?' Can you believe him?"

"One more loop?" Peter said.

"Don't you have homework?"

"One more. To celebrate." He kicked off down a rocky slope.

To the left and right of the bike trail, precious black crust—cryptobiotic soil—crawled across the sand. The stew of bacteria, fungi, algae, moss, and lichen clumped together, fixing the surface and absorbing water and nutrients to feed the desert. But one footstep, one cloven cow print, could crush a hundred years' worth of work building the protective layer. A cow herd could destroy acres of crypto in a day.

Peter climbed a steep rise thirty yards ahead of Tara. She never used to have trouble keeping up with him. When she graduated in three weeks, she would look for real work, quit her part-time jobs teaching at the university and leading bike tours. She and Peter would move into a bigger apartment. He wouldn't have to sleep on a couch anymore.

Claret cup cactus blossoms dotted the mesa with splashes of red among the scattered pinyons and junipers where the crypto thrived. Tara stood up in her pedals, pumping harder to block out the image of Burns' herd crushing the delicate soil.

"You're prioritizing the needs of creatures so small, you can't even see them, over my family's livelihood." Burns had touched the rim of his cowboy hat like an exclamation point. He had been the last one to question her as she defended her research. In his arrogance, Chester Burns always got the last word.

"But one family is not more important than an entire ecosystem, sir." The word sir still tasted bitter on her tongue hours after she spoke it.

She caught a flash of Pete's bike as he spun off the slickrock onto a rocky switchback heading toward the parking lot.

"Mom!" Peter's wail poured over her like ice water, as a clatter of falling rock crashed around the bend.

Gravity obeyed different rules in the desert. Rocks that looked poised to tumble, teetered for decades without falling, while solid plates of time-burnished sandstone sheared off canyon walls without warning.

Tara sped around the switchback as a boulder smashed down, just feet away from where Peter lay, not moving. She skidded on the loose rock and slid sideways, gravel shredding skin from her thigh. She caught a whiff of desert rose and a flash of buttery blossoms just as her ankle snapped.

"Peter." She crawled toward to him.

His chest rose and fell, but he did not respond.

The pain in Tara's ankle blinded her as she tried to put weight on it. Her bent front wheel wouldn't turn when she tried to lean on the bike as a rolling crutch.

The silence of the remote desert pounded in her temples.

"I'm going for help. Don't move," she scratched a message into 200-million-year-old sandstone with a piece of chert. She touched her son's sweaty cheek with her dry lips, took a swallow of water, and left her bottle for Peter.

If she bypassed the mile-long, serpentine bike trail and cut a direct line across the mesa – across the crypto—she might make it before sunset. Before the coyotes and bobcats came prowling.

Instead, she crept backwards like a three-legged crab down the meandering, rocky path. Tara craned her neck to watch Peter's slumped form until he disappeared. She couldn't look at her throbbing foot, hanging at an unnatural angle, without gagging.

Claret cups closed their blossoms as the sun dipped. Her shadow stretched to a fragile sheath pointing toward her car.

Tara shifted off trail. With a crunch like a million tiny bones breaking, she sunk a bare hand into the meaty crypto and dragged herself in a straight line toward the parking lot.

Scarlet Letter, No More

Joani Peacock

Mea culpa. Mea culpa. Mea maxima culpa.

For 45 years, I have locked my secret away in a vault.

Lead lined, buried deep, for me and me alone, always to keep and never to tell.
Under lock and key, it seemed safer that way.

Forty-five years ago, just sixteen years old, I went looking for love, wherever I could find it.

And it wasn't at home.

Outside looking in, I was Doctor Peacock's daughter, well to do, parochial school girl, goody two shoes, and middle child.

Inside looking out, I parented myself from a very early age. While my alcoholic bipolar mom was behind closed doors and my workaholic dad was forever making rounds, I learned to take care of Joani.

So I found love in the boy next door. Both refugees from our dysfunctional households, close friends, we clung to one another for love and support.
And then I was "late." Oh my God, Oh my God, what have I done?

1972. Alone and disowned by my parents, I had become a disgrace. A shame on my family, impossible to erase.

Should we have a shotgun wedding? My parents said no. His parents said yes. But both sets agreed that teenage parents, we were destined to be.

But I was a minor, just a child myself. And though I had conceived this child, I could not possibly conceive of being a mom at 17. No, not yet. No, not now. No visible means of support. No diploma. No degree. Not even a bank account to call my own.

I was terrified. Out and out terrified.

Scarlet Letter, No More (Joani Peacock)

A junior in high school, at Immaculata Prep, I hid my belly beneath a sweater, buttoned up well into the spring. And on May 19th of '72, the priest having refused us, we were married at the courthouse by the Justice of the Peace. I bought a calico hippie, peasant dress for the occasion but my mother insisted I wear white.

I might as well have worn a Scarlet Letter.

And though I knew I could not keep her, I also knew I had to bring her into this world.

The social worker at the adoption agency, whose name I wish I could remember, mothered me three trimesters through. But it was 1972. There was no Planned Parenthood. No birthing classes. No Lamaze. Just a stick figure pamphlet from the Medicaid clinic.

I remember going to the public library to find a picture book, so I could see and understand what was happening inside of me. Blushing at the circulation desk, I was terrified to actually check it out.

September 28th of '72, in a cab all by myself, I made it to my final appointment at Georgetown Hospital. Already in labor, the nurse rushed me to the delivery room. No time for drugs. I did nothing but push.

And out she came: purple and slippery and squawking and full of life. Shaking and in shock, I could not bring myself to hold her. I knew that if I did, I risked not giving her up.

I had no plans to even name her, for she was never going to be mine. But the birth certificate sat on my tray table. I had to fill in the blanks. Elizabeth Catherine. Or was it Elizabeth Beatrice? I can't quite remember.

But I did visit the nursery, though I did not go inside.

"Please, hold her up to the window for me, so that I can see her before I go."

"Goodbye, little Elizabeth. I wish you a good life. I wish you the best it can be."

And I have never regretted this decision. I am proud of that child that brought this child into the world in 1972.

So I signed the papers, a sealed adoption. She would never know us and we would never know her. It seemed best for all concerned. And what did I know? I was only seventeen.

So I locked the secret up tight and threw away the key. Grieving was a luxury I could not afford. Traumatized teenagers, kicked to the curb, we had to survive.

So I skipped my senior year and a year or so later, I made it to CUA. We got jobs in a preschool and the tiniest efficiency you have ever seen.

And now, to make a long story short, we took ten years to grow up. Built a marriage. Built a home. Built a life. And ten years later, in 1982, we had Zach and then Colleen and then Jacob.

All three babies made possible by Elizabeth, the baby I never held in my arms.

And even to my three children, she was a secret. Locked up tight. Never to tell.

Why? What good would it do? What would I say? What purpose would it serve? Forty-five years is a very long time. It seemed the vault would hold forever.

And then she found me.

Through a DNA test on Ancestry.com (my brother's account), just before Christmas, she found me.

An emotional tsunami broke loose in my head. Pummeled by waves, I was certain I'd drown. Buoyed by therapy, I did not.

Rebecca Dragon is her name: mother of three. Lives on a farm in Vermont. Spiritual seeker. Russian Orthodox, by choice. Theater major. She found and read my blog. My daughter's too.

Excited beyond words, she had found her tribe.

Terrified beyond words, I froze, not knowing what I would do.

But, of course, I did.

The next morning, I called her. The hardest phone call I have ever made in my life.

We talked for half an hour. Crying. Incredulous. Laughing. And now, we have talked many more times. Texting, emailing, FaceBooking, too.
Scarlet Letter, No More (Joani Peacock)

She is happy, healthy, and whole. A down to earth, sort of off-the-grid parent, she home schools her three children. Crafty, she spins and knits. Comfortable in the kitchen, she makes real food from scratch. She is snarky and hysterical, theological and spiritual, and a blogger, herself, twice over. An urban expat, living on a rural route, she grew up in D.C.

Though those domestic genes are certainly not mine, she reminds me so much of me. Different, of course: taller, green eyes, and a different nose. She is definitely one of us. Primarily a Peacock, I would vainly say.

DNA is much more powerful than I ever could have imagined.

And now my children know and have happily connected with her, too. And my siblings know. And my coworkers know, as well as my friends.

And now you know too.

Saint Patrick's Day weekend, I flew to Vermont to meet Rebecca and her children: Bella, Jude, and Meir, and her husband, too.

I arrived as "just Joani." I am not "mom" or "grandma." Rebecca's fabulous parents, alone, deserve these titles. I did not raise her as my own. I like to call her, "my long lost offspring," and as for me, "biomom," at least for now.

But we are definitely biologically joined at the hip. And I really, really like her. (Dare I say love her?) And I look forward to knowing her and her family, more and more.

So the "Peacock and the Dragon" have met. We'll take it from here.

No more "Mea maxima culpa."

Scarlet Letter no more.

In The Land of Enchantment

Kelli Sullivan

Clarissa

Clarissa watched as her younger sisters enjoyed the games at the Community Center Spring Festival, but relay races didn't interest her. The net at the top of the ceiling showed promise; it was bursting with more balloons than Clarissa had ever seen, and in the prettiest shades that captured the dazzling colors of the New Mexico sky.

"Twilight Lilac," she repeated to herself in a whisper, and she shared her observation with the lady in charge. "How clever you are!" the lady clasped her hands together in delight, and she stopped pouring lemonade into little paper cups. She and Clarissa strolled around the airy gymnasium, their eyes to the sky lit ceiling, comparing their individual impressions and, together, came up with names for all of the colors. The pale purple was Clarissa's favorite.

The most marvelous thing happened about fifteen minutes later, after the lady gave a signal. Some grown-ups pulled on ropes connected to the net at the ceiling, and suddenly the room became a vivid flurry of red, blue orange, and purple. Clarissa knew she was getting too old to play Pretend, but she waded into the ocean of balloons anyway, laughing and twirling, imagining herself in a storybook where characters lived on fluffy clouds colored Sunrise Yellow, Firestorm Red, and Twilight Lilac.

Clarissa thrived on stories, especially the kind with magic, and her fifth-grade teacher, Miss Vasquez, had a talent for finding used books to fuel her imagination. They were a struggling community, but Clarissa would rather have books than toys, or even the trendy clothes and makeup that some of the girls her age talked about. Her parents, Ana and Alex, were bewildered by their unusual, dreamy-eyed daughter. Why was she always reading and looking off into the clouds? Miss Vasquez assured them that Clarissa was her brightest student and that books were the key to a better future, so they encouraged her to keep learning, and especially, to keep reading.

As she was leaving the party with her family, Clarissa's little sister Patricia skipped over and handed her a pale purple balloon that volunteers had filled with helium and tied to a silver ribbon. "Clarissa!" she bubbled, "look what they are giving us to take home!"

"Twilight Lilac," Clarissa murmured.

Clarissa began to fantasize about a steady, desert wind guiding the balloon to a faraway place, which in her mind was Mt. Olympus, a city in the clouds, and she remembered what she learned about helium in science class. She understood that if she released the balloon, it would continue to rise while the pressure inside caused it to expand. Eventually, the balloon would explode, unless it started leaking, or there was a storm. *Then it might not reach Olympus at all.* Well, these are the scientific facts. *But wouldn't it be wonderful if something magical happened instead? What if it floated into Zeus' Hall, and the gods were having an important council in the sunset-colored clouds—wouldn't they wonder how that balloon got there? Maybe they'd send Percy Jackson on a mission to find out!* She smiled as she watched the balloon sway in the afternoon breeze, preoccupied in her imagination, while her parents led the family home.

That night while the house slept, Clarissa took the Sharpie pen Miss Vasquez had loaned her to make posters for the school book drive. She closed her eyes, made a wish, and wrote a message on the Twilight Lilac balloon. Clarissa climbed onto the desk in the bedroom she shared with her sisters, opened the window and scooted her body out halfway, grunting as she scraped her stomach on the metal frame. She let go of the balloon and twisted around, so that lying on her back, she could watch it rise into the starry sky and fly away to the home of the gods.

Ruthie

If there was one thing Ruthie Watson had learned in her fifty-five years, it was to stay out of other people's business. She lived alone with her two dogs on her government pension in a house that had belonged to her father. Ruthie worked as a mail carrier for the city of Albuquerque for thirty-five years, but now she scheduled her days around her two favorite things: peace and quiet, both of which gave her time to read and time to enjoy her dogs.

Half a lifetime spent walking for a living had yet to dampen her enthusiasm for the activity, and on this particular April morning, the thermometer on the suction cup stuck to her kitchen window registered a refreshing 70 degrees. At 8:00 am on the dot, Ruthie changed into khaki shorts and an old sweatshirt and wrestled a baseball cap onto her mop of thick, grey curls. She leashed up her wiggling German Shepherds, Rhett and Scarlet, and the three stepped out onto Hummingbird Lane for a long, energizing walk.

Scarlet saw it first, the purple balloon bumping along the sidewalk, and she abruptly sat on her haunches, mystified. The sparkly silver ribbon appeared to be tangled in the Cimarron Sage growing on the median next to the sidewalk. As Ruthie and Rhett were cheerfully marching along to the rhythm of their own thoughts, this counter-pull caused Ruthie to trip and Rhett to get tangled up in Scarlet's leash, his own leash, and Ruthie's dancing legs.

"Scarlet! Rhett! What in the...?" exclaimed Ruthie, as she smacked the concrete, scraping her palms and banging up her knee. "You silly dogs!"

"Woof," offered Scarlet, staring at the balloon, and she crept closer for a better sniff and perhaps a little bite.

"A balloon? No, Scarlet! Leave it!"

But as Ruthie sat up and disentangled herself from the dogs, she noticed what seemed to be a message on the deflated remains of the balloon. Curious, she leaned forward and slowly made out, "This is a wish for a complete set of *Percy Jackson and the Olympians.* Thank you, signed Clarissa Moreno."

"I'll be darned!" said Ruthie. Both dogs looked at her. "Now that's definitely a new one, wishing on a balloon," she said. *The little girl must be an eager reader. Well I hope, somehow, she gets her books.* She untangled the leashes so they could finish their walk.

"Woof!" insisted Scarlet, unwilling to leave her prize.

"Come on, girl, let's go." Ruthie commanded, but Scarlet, like her legendary namesake, had a mind of her own. "Oh, alright, you stubborn creature!" Exasperated, Ruthie picked up the balloon.

A mile away, Elizabeth waited in a hanging wicker swing on Ruthie's front porch. She was practicing some breathing exercises her life coach had recommended, more to be of service to Elizabeth's family and friends than to Elizabeth, herself. When Ruthie and the dogs finally materialized, she jumped up to intercept her sister, concern quashing the smallest hint of impatience. Ruthie listed to the right, her bloody leg looking somewhat pulpy.

"What happened?" She breathed. "Are you alright?"

"Fine," Ruther sighed and regarded Elizabeth, all hair-sprayed and made-up and alarmingly taut with potential energy. "I tripped, but it's just some scrapes. Come inside while I clean up."

"Should I call Dr. Hardy just in case? I popped over to check on you before my meeting. Any coffee leftover from breakfast?" Elizabeth asked.

"Lizzie, how many pots have you had already?" Ruthie muttered. "Help yourself."

Scarlet and Rhett visited the water bowl while Elizabeth ignored her sister's sarcasm and followed Ruthie to her bathroom, an enormous, steaming mug requiring both of her French-manicured hands. "What's with the balloon?" she asked, as she placed her coffee on the counter and stretched the latex back and forth to read the message.

Ruthie had forgotten to toss the blasted object. "Just something Scarlet found on the walk. Some kind of prank." Elizabeth was easing back into her routine after another miscarriage, and Ruthie believed the last thing her sister needed today was someone else's problem. She squirted her scuffed-up palms with hydrogen peroxide and globbed Neosporin on her leg while stealing glances at Elizabeth, whose emotions always played right across her face.

Elizabeth stared at Ruthie. "Is this not the saddest thing ever?"

Ruthie touched Elizabeth's shoulder gently. "Lizzie. You don't always have to be everyone's Fairy Godmother."

"Ruthie! We simply must find this child!" Elizabeth's honest-to-God sincerity was an incidental weapon for coaxing her society friends to open their wallets for her latest causes. "And what if 'god-mother' is the closest I get to having another child?"

Ruthie regretted her choice of words, but maneuvered to avoid the Dark Place this beautiful morning. "Oh, come on Lizzie! It's probably a kid so you can't just Google her! And what if it's some weirdo?"

"Well, let's start with local elementary schools," Elizabeth decided.

"No school will give out student information to a stranger!" said Ruthie.

"Ruthie." Elizabeth grinned, "give me some credit. I play tennis with the superintendent!"

"Lizzie, do we even know the kid is local, if in fact it is an actual kid? Can't balloons float for, like, hundreds of miles? And anyway, I have zero desire to get involved with some needy child and her family!"

"Ruthie, how can you say that?" Elizabeth was passionate now. "All this poor girl is asking for is a set of books for heaven's sake! Can you imagine the desperation? We have to find out what kind of circumstances she's living in; this child may need our help."

Ruthie finished her disinfecting and walked determinedly back to the den. Elizabeth followed, draining her mug, and working up to a battle pitch.

"What are the chances! I mean, you finding Clarissa's balloon this morning and me just happening to stop by. Give it to me. I am making it my personal mission to locate this child and change her life!"

Elizabeth's high heels clicked resolutely across the hardwood floor, and Ruthie heard her sing out a cheery farewell to the dogs before slamming the front door.

Ruthie rolled her eyes to the ceiling, but she acknowledged the motivation behind Elizabeth's relentless desire to set the world right. "Well, heaven knows if anyone can find the girl, it's Lizzy," Ruthie said to Scarlet and Rhett. She settled into her armchair and contemplated an ambitious stack of books on the table next to her.

Three weeks later, Ruthie was down to the last book in her pile.

"Well, I must admit this is harder than I thought," Elizabeth was saying. "I even called Hank Willoughby; you know, the Chief Meteorologist for Channel 7? Anyway, he said it would be hard to pinpoint exactly where the balloon was released because there are so many variables and we don't know exactly when she let it go!"

"Uh huh," said Ruthie, who was savoring the final fifty pages of the latest James Patterson novel when Elizabeth called. In for the long haul, she had placed her cell on speaker phone ten minutes ago, and laid it on the adjacent table.

"I wanted to have this figured out before we left town." Ruthie heard the tone shift in Elizabeth's voice, and put the phone back to her ear. "Arthur and my sweet Bobby have been angels, putting up with all of my moodiness. You too, Ruthie. But you know how it kills me to give up on anything."

"Oh Lizzie," Ruthie sighed, "just go and have fun, and we'll talk about this when you get back."

Ruthie and Clarissa

Clarissa sat next to Miss Vasquez at the Frio River Elementary School book drive table in the brand-new bookshop. It was a Saturday morning, but she wore her school uniform, and her hair was neatly oiled and braided. Clarissa hadn't realized that new books smelled different from old ones. She wandered the aisles, pulling out books and reading the summaries on their cover jackets, hoping that some would end up in their school library, until Miss Vasquez told her the store was about to open and she needed to take her place at the table. Clarissa had tried to stop thinking about her balloon, but sometimes when she was falling asleep, she imagined Percy Jackson combing the Chihuahua Desert, desperately trying to find her.

Earlier that morning, Ruthie had looked at her empty book table, and felt a hankering for a good old-fashioned saga. She read in the newspaper about a new bookshop opening about 20 minutes away, not terribly convenient, but the ad featured a coupon with a big discount that was too tempting to pass up. When she arrived, she saw the sign asking for donations to the elementary school, but Ruthie had all but forgotten about Clarissa Moreno. She noticed the little girl with the shiny black hair and the innocent brown eyes and was surprised when her legs walked her over and planted her squarely in front of the child.

Miss Vasquez was thanking some book donors, sharing her dream for a more appealing library at Frio River Elementary, so Clarissa greeted the lady with the curly grey hair and the funny look on her face.

"Good morning, ma'am," the child said, "my name is Clarissa, and I love to read!"

"Hello Clarissa, my name is Ruthie," she offered cautiously, "and I love to read too. What's your favorite book?" The words were out of her mouth before she had time to stop herself. Surely this could not be The Clarissa!

"Oh, that's easy," Clarissa said. "My favorite is *Percy Jackson and the Lightening Thief!* But one day I'd like to read all of the books in the series because I want to know how it all ends."

In the sweetness of Clarissa's young voice, Ruthie heard another; it was still a child's voice, but one that was filled with a much different kind of longing.

The memory had momentum now, and she felt an unexpected stab of the despair she had so carefully buried with her mother years ago. Little Lizzie was just five years old, gripping Ruthie's hand and saying, "Tell me again, Ruthie. I want to know how it's all going to end, when we are back with Mommy and she's not dead anymore." Ruthie was just 17. She had tried to catch her father's eye, but he stood apart from his daughters, as stiff and uncomfortable in his misery as he was in the dark wool suit he wore on that hot summer day. She turned back to her sister, Lizzie's sweetness and confusion and innocence all laid at Ruthie's feet like an offering, and from that day forward, Ruthie carried the burden of Lizzie's grief along with her own.

Ruthie blinked at Clarissa, fished in her handbag for a twenty to put in the cash donation box, and turned to go. She had a sudden need for space.

"Miss Ruthie?" asked Clarissa, so Ruthie turned around. "What's your favorite book?"

Ruthie managed a smile. "When I was your age, my favorite book was *The Lion, The Witch and the Wardrobe.* It's a story about magic, too."

Clarissa's smile was a ray of sunshine. "Oh, I like the sound of that! Will you please tell me more about it?"

Ruthie was unnerved. Clarissa's easy intimacy made her uncomfortable, but something kept her feet rooted to that rubbery-smelling carpet rolling out from under the Frio River Elementary School book drive table. *What a pure soul is this strange little girl!* Perhaps it was because no one has asked about her favorite *anything* in such a long time, or maybe it was the rawness of the old feelings mixed up with Clarissa's sincerity, the child struggling so desperately to connect with someone who might understand her. But as Ruthie continued to chat with Clarissa, she realized that she was, in fact, exactly where she wanted to be. And that it felt surprisingly good. She smiled, imagining what Elizabeth would say.

"Miss Ruthie," asked Clarissa, a bit shyly for the first time, "do you believe in magic? I mean, did you ever?"

Ruthie paused and swallowed the lump. "Well Clarissa, I think I would like to give believing another try. Because I have the most wonderful story to tell you about my dog Scarlet, and my sister Elizabeth, and a purple balloon; and in this story, Clarissa, you are the one with the magic."

Signals

PJ Devlin

It's 11:40 a.m. Percy and a baby-faced brunette in a striped sweater and skinny jeans laugh as they trip up the steps to his third floor apartment. Mrs. Sanchez, dark and silent, stands on the landing holding a basket of white hand-towels she embroiders with blue flowers.

"Hola!" Percy says when they push past her.

As soon as they burst into his apartment, Percy locks the door, drops his backpack, and then wraps his arms around the brunette's waist and twirls her completely around. The girl spins onto the worn brown sofa that smells of coffee. She grabs Percy's backpack and drops a thin book into it.

"A gift," she says.

Percy smiles, then looks around, feeling watched. On the kitchen wall, a Kit-Cat clock rolls its eyes back and forth.

"I'll be back," he says and goes into the bathroom.

In the mirror, he bares his teeth like a dog, swigs mouthwash and spits. With a deep breath, he returns to the living room. The girl walks around the room picking up odds and ends. She stares at the photograph of Percy and Peggy at the top of a Ferris Wheel.

"She must be nice," the girl says. "Is she really that fat?"

Percy doesn't want to think about Peggy. He wants to have fun, to laugh, to do whatever the hell he wants.

"You ready to work on calculus?" he asks.

The girl takes his hand and leads him to the sofa. She lies back and pulls him on top.

"Let's work on integration," she says.

Percy leans on his elbows and looks in her eyes. Her breath smells of cigarettes and juicy-fruit gum. She takes off her sweater, and its blue-white-blue stripes remind Percy of a signal flag he memorized in the Navy—On fire, keep clear. Her hands run under his shirt, across his back, and over his ass. She slides them below his navel and tugs at his zipper. He feels pain on his chest near his heart, where her breath is hot and moist, and he likes the pain.

"Integration," he whispers, "the analysis of functions with..in con..tin..u..ous do..mains."

He feels on fire and knows he should keep clear, but his head explodes and he lets everything go—guilt, responsibility, trust.

***

While the girl uses the bathroom, Percy uses his Pearl Jam T-shirt to dry the sofa cushions and decides to flip them over. He looks at the clock then goes to the bedroom and tosses his damp shirt and red boxers in the hamper. From a pile on the floor he grabs a white T-shirt and goes commando in his faded jeans.

In the kitchen, the girl licks peanut butter off a knife. Her head goes back and forth, following the Kit-Cat clock's eyes. Calculus class is in thirty minutes. Percy checks the living room then ushers the girl out the door. Mrs. Sanchez passes them on the stairs. Percy's glad she doesn't speak English.

***

It's 7:15 p.m. Percy opens the apartment door to red boxers flapping like the signal flag— Discharging explosives. Inside, Peggy stands like a fighter. She throws the boxers in his face and then rips through a hole in his Pearl Jam T-shirt and drops it on the floor. He crosses the threshold laughing.

"What's wrong with you?" he asks.

Percy brushes against her, hangs his keys on the hook by the door, drops his backpack, and lays his laptop on the coffee table. His blond hair is tousled and his beard is gritty.

Peggy's red hair frames a face covered with amber freckles the color of her eyes. Her lips draw tight across the overbite he used to think was cute. Soft skin cushions her arms and legs—her body's no longer the physically fit one she flaunted before he married her. She clenches her jaw and spits out her words.

"I watched you put on these boxers this morning. Now I find them in the hamper—wet and nasty. Your toothbrush is wet too. When did you come back to the apartment, Percy? Why'd you change your clothes?"

He looks shocked and sad, tilts his head and blinks. A festering smell rises from his armpits and he concentrates on keeping his expression hurt and innocent.

"The Bio professor cancelled class, so I came home, jogged, took a shower, grabbed a PB&J, and drove back to school. What's the big deal?"

He smiles, puts his hands on her shoulders and gazes into her eyes. The fragrance of White Linen floats from her clothes. When he bends to kiss her, she backs away. His mouth tastes of cigarettes and the girl.

"Look, Peggy, between studying and working out, Baby, I got nothing left for anyone but you. You better now? Hungry? I'm starving. What's to eat?"

Percy goes to the refrigerator, grabs a tub of macaroni and cheese and slides it into the microwave. On the brown velveteen sofa from her parents' house, Peggy tucks herself in a corner. He hears her quiet sobs. Their bed, a mattress on the floor, came from her parents, too. The sheets are crumpled like they left them this morning when she ran to catch the bus to her job in DC and he drove her car to campus. She's still in her work clothes. Her wrinkled white blouse hangs over a black skirt straining against her waist. Peggy looks more like her mother every day and Percy wonders what he got himself into.

"I'll be back. Gotta take a leak."

Percy leans into the mirror. Stupid to ditch his nasty clothes. Peggy's powers of observation leap quantums beyond those of the most highly trained spy in the universe. His blue eyes peer out above dark circles. He brushes his teeth and tongue to remove the yeasty taste, pitches his shirt and runs a towel over his chest. When he raises his arms, he smells sex. Deodorant coats a fresh sheen across his armpits and he feels better. At the microwave's chirp, he walks shirtless to the kitchen. He doesn't notice the purple mark near his heart.

Percy fills two bowls with macaroni swimming in Velveeta and carries them to the living room. He offers the smaller bowl to Peggy but she shakes her head, no. He retreats to the bean bag chair to eat both bowls and he's still hungry.

"Did you go shopping?" His smile is charming and boyish, designed for absolution.

"No, Percy, but apparently you did. Was it worth it? Did you get your money's worth?"

Her face flushes with patches of white and red, and he thinks of the flag signal—You are running into danger. White noise buzzes his head.

Percy crosses to the sofa, sits next to Peggy and rubs his cheek on her arm, adopting the tactics discussed late into the night with his buddies on the super-carrier, USS Harry Truman. Peggy's head twitches like a compass needle trying to find north.

"You must think I'm stupid. God, you never even take out the trash but today you come home to rearrange cushions and change your clothes?"

Percy sees hurt coursing off her body like heat. If he reaches out, he'll touch it.

"Look, a girl from my calculus class flunked the mid-term and asked me to go over derivatives with her. I thought we'd concentrate better if we had a quiet place to study, so we came here. I spilled a soda on myself and the sofa so I changed before we went back to campus. I didn't tell you because I knew you'd go psycho. There's never anything good to eat around here. When do you get paid?"

"Goddamn it, Percy. You take my car. Would it kill you to pick up groceries once in awhile? I bust my ass to pay the rent while you bring some girl here to help with calculus. Maybe you should help me once in awhile." Peggy glares at him from amber eyes that flash yellow like a panther's. The dignity in her rage frightens him.

"In a year I'll get my engineering degree, then I'll make good money. I don't have rich parents like you to put me through college. While you went to football games and got drunk at parties, I protected this country. Now it's my turn. You knew what you were getting into when you married me."

"I had no idea what I was getting into. You begged me to get married. You cried and said all you thought about when you were out to sea was coming home to marry me. You didn't give a damn about my plan to work a year then go to law school. Why was it so important to get married right away?"

His blue eyes burn with fatigue. Everything's so hard. He rubs his right biceps where a tattooed lion roars above a striking snake and takes a deep breath.

"I thought I'd lose you," he whispers.

The macaroni and cheese form a lump in his stomach and he wants to vomit. His hands tremble. Percy crossed the room to Peggy, takes her arms and drapes them on his shoulders. She pushes him away.

Her chin juts out and her lip quivers. "After work, I rush home to be with you. But you're never here. You stay late on campus to go out with your friends. When you do come home, you've bought yourself pizza or tacos but you never bring anything for me."

He raises his eyebrows and his eyes open wide. "You never told me you wanted tacos."

"Oh my God," she says and punches him in the chest.

Percy slinks away to slump in the beanbag chair. He's still hungry and doesn't want to deal with this shit.

"It's no fun anymore, Peggy. You're always tired and you're always pissed. You have to know where I'm going, who I'm with, when I'll be home. You want to control everything I do. I had more freedom when I was in the Navy."

"What do you think it means to be married, Percy?"

He is sick of this conversation, sick of her expectations, her demands, her petty calculations of who does what, who pays for what.

"I don't think it should mean I have to get your permission before I go out or do anything. I love you but the more you nag, the less I want to be here. I don't want a mother." The anger in his voice shocks him.

"A mother is exactly what you want. You want me to pay the bills, clean the apartment, wash your clothes, buy your food, and make your dinner while you come and go as you please. What about what I want? You care more about a skanky teenage girl than you do about me." Tears run down her cheeks, but she looks angry, not sorrowful.

The soft vinyl of the beanbag is warm from his flesh and reeks of beer. He runs his fingers through his hair, then rubs them on his jeans and thinks it's time to go to the Laundromat and wash everything, every piece of clothing, every towel, every sheet. Start clean and fresh. He opens his mouth to tell her this but he's infuriated when she opens his backpack and pulls out the book that pathetic loser gave him—Jonathan Livingston Seagull. Peggy reads the inscription out loud: Keep working on love. Begin by knowing you have already arrived. Thanks for being a great teacher. ♥Sandy.

Peggy rips out the page, crumbles it and throws it at him, then hurls the book like a Frisbee. It jams into the lion on his arm. "It's time you tell the truth," she says.

Percy's back and ass ache from sitting on the beanbag chair. This is a critical moment. He should ponder the problem and consider independent variables that influence the outcome. It's the random variable that worries him.

"We're going through a tough time, Pegs. You're busy, I'm busy. We're running in different directions. We hardly ever have sex. I know, maybe I'm trying to make up for everything I missed by joining the Navy. This sophomore girl, Sandy, has been flirting with me all semester. Anyway, I brought her here to study, only to study. I never cheated, Peggy, I swear. But when she pulled me close, honestly, I was tempted. I felt her lips but when I thought about you, I pushed her away. She was so pissed. She called me a loser and hurled her soda at me. It got all over my clothes and all over the sofa. I wanted to punch her, but I just changed my clothes, wiped up the spills, turned over the cushions, and drove her back to campus. Whatever you think, I'm glad it happened. It was a test, and I passed. I choose you, Peggy. For better, for worse, in good times and bad, I choose you."

Percy takes Peggy in his arms. Her tears trickle down his chest. He smoothes her hair and touches her face. He loves her soft skin. Peggy's the only thing in his life that matters. His resentment turns to sympathy and understanding. Desire. Near his heart, her finger traces a circle, over and over. It excites him.

Percy steers her to the bedroom and caresses her until she stops trembling. He feels powerful and heroic, with his arm a pillow for Peggy's head and the taste of her tears a salty completion. He sleeps in deep oblivion, floating in an ocean of childhood dreams.

***

It's 9:10 am. The sun angles through the window, piercing his eyes like daggers. He burrows under the blanket and breathes the essence of Peggy's body.

"Peg?" he calls.

Percy kicks off the sheets but stays in bed, reliving last night. It's true what they say about make-up sex. His stomach growls. He hopes Peggy woke up early, got dressed quietly so as not to wake him and any minute, will walk into the apartment with cups of sweet coffee, cinnamon bagels oozing cream cheese and the newspaper. He feels himself rise at the thought of her setting down their breakfast then jumping into bed with him. He has class at 11:00 but would blow it off for another time with Peggy. Damn, she must have gone to work.

He rolls out of bed, goes to the bathroom and decides to take a shower, wash his hair and start on the clean sweep their relationship needs. He squeezes a glob of Peggy's lavender-rose shampoo on his hair and sticks out his tongue to taste the soapy water as it cascades down his face. He cleans himself with her oatmeal soap, the tiny grains rough against his skin. With water tapping his head, he sits in the tub and scrubs his calloused feet. Peggy always says he should get a pedicure and maybe he will—with bright nail polish to make her laugh. He takes her pink razor and trims under his arms. Percy dries himself with the only towel on the rack, a white hand-towel embroidered with blue flowers. After he combs back his hair, he notices his hairline receding. Above the dark circles, his blue eyes gleam clear.

Percy feels better than he has in months. Today he'll tell Sandy they had a lot of fun but his wife suspects and he won't risk it. He wonders how he could be so stupid, bringing her here for sex. He's just damned lucky Peggy believes him. *Don't bother me anymore*, he'll tell the girl. *You mean nothing to me.*

He finds white briefs in the back of his drawer and pulls on the khakis he wears when he has to get dressed up. The only clean shirt in the closet is a green polo he hates, but he slides it over his head. He wants something to eat.

On the kitchen wall, the Kit-Cat clock's eyes go back and forth and it creeps him out. The refrigerator's empty. He'll be ten minutes late if he leaves now.

He'll come home right after class. They'll go shopping tonight, maybe grab some burgers then stock up at the store. They'll buy good food—vegetables and fruit, apples and strawberries, stuff to make salad and a Chablis. This weekend they'll cook together and Sunday, he'll take Peggy to the Art Museum.

The living room looks strangely sterile. On the sofa, the cushions lay askew but he can't put his finger on what's different. Percy studies the apartment he entered as Peggy's husband—the walls he painted yellow, the worn sofa, the beanbag chair from his childhood bedroom, the photo of them at the top of the Ferris Wheel, where he asked her to marry him and she said yes, where they looked down at the foamy surf smashing on the beach and touched infinity where the sky met the sea in a line so narrow it disappeared.

On the hook by the door, the car keys are gone. Percy sits on the sofa and reaches for his laptop. Across the smooth white surface, the girl's red and yellow thong twists through Peggy's wedding ring.

Percy sinks at the signal—*Man Overboard.*

This story orginally appeared in the anthology "Abundant Grace" in 2016.

The Road to Heaven

Brandon French

It was the same old sad-ass rhetoric. Blah-blah-blah-God-grant-me-blah-blah. Principles-not-personalities-blah-blah-blah. These jokers had it memorized like Catholic school boys reciting their Hail Mary's. One step at a time. Let go and let God. They repeated it right up until their next snort, next fix, or next pill.

Sandra sighed. This was her regular Friday night NA meeting at the Episcopalian Church Community Room in Hollywood but she wished she was home watching Bill Maher. She was a recovering pill head with sixteen months' sobriety, although a rookie compared to some of the other druggies, several of whom had reached the pinnacle of 80 Oxy's a day. She'd kept steady at 20, sweetened with vodka and benzos when life pressed too hard. Oxy's were like shots of bliss, the blasphemous answer to her Serenity Prayer. She called them "the Big Aahhhhhh" because they loosened every clenched organ inside of her and provided a momentary sensation of invincibility. But for the last year-and-a-half, she'd been managing to drum her knuckles without them.

Tonight, though, something was juggling her guts.

There were a few new faces in the room. One guy in particular with red streaks in his hair like Indian war paint. He looked around at everyone with a wise, kindly smile, an old man's smile on a relatively young man's face. Compassionate. He was tall, a handsome man despite the streaks, with large, light brown eyes flecked with gold.

Sandra chose not to share. What was she going to say? That living life without opiates sometimes felt like sliding bare-belly over a bed of hot coals? That being a divorced, recently retired UCLA Renaissance specialist who lived alone on a pension was not exactly the destiny she had envisioned for herself? Should she reveal to a room full of ragtag losers that, over the last decade, everything had fallen? Her breasts. Her arches. The skin beneath her chin. Her expectations. Her eyelids. Her value as a person. Couldn't they already see that it lay in a heap at her feet like a soggy swimsuit on the worn blue linoleum floor?

The new guy, Red Streaks, raised his hand to share. His parents, a career

Army officer and a nurse, threw him out on the streets of Washington, D.C. when he was fifteen because he was gay, he says. Gay. Okay. There went that little spark of hope, although, let's get serious, she was sixty-seven, old enough to be his mother even if he was close to forty. Maybe his older sister? Who was she kidding, his mother. He became a sex worker, he says. Prostitute. Got Hep B. Hep C. Not AIDS, although that was a miracle. What kind of people kick a fifteen-year-old kid into the street because he's gay? Bastards. Sandra had a thing about parents throwing their children to the wolves when they didn't approve of their behavior.

"That's what God did to Lucifer, his 'child of light' for shit's sake," Sandra said as she and her sponsor Gwen, a tall, stout mountain of a woman wearing laundry-bleached lavender sweats, were heading over to the coffee urn at the end of the meeting. "All because the boy refused to bow down to his baby brother Jesus. Wiped his hands of the kid. Turned him into Satan, who was 'hurled headlong' from heaven, according to Milton, for his disobedience."

Gwen was used to being lectured to by Sandra, who missed having halls full of adoring students to regale now that she had retired. Gwen herself had spent thirty years teaching English lit to black and Hispanic teenagers, the last few at a charter high school in South L.A. where she was finally allowed to design her own curriculum –- Carver, Johnson, Dybek, Tobias Wolff, Jhumpa Lahiri, ZZ Packer, and some dazzling newbies like Clare Vaye Watkins and Adam Johnson. The freedom was even more intoxicating than the cocaine she snorted each day, she'd explained at an NA speakers' meeting, and after a decade alone, she had finally met the second love of her life, the twelve-years-sober Lenore. So, early one winter morning, three years, four months and six days ago ("but who's counting?"), Gwen woke up, took a hot shower and decided it was time to get clean.

"It's a shit job, being a parent," Gwen said, as the coffee line inched toward the table.

"That's why I never wanted to be one," Sandra said. "I was pretty sure I'd fuck it up."

Red Streaks reached the urn ahead of them and filled a Styrofoam cup. He offered it amiably to either of the women, and Gwen reached out first. He filled another cup for Sandra and a third for himself, causing the people behind them in line to grumble impatiently.

"I loved your share," Sandra said, not remembering his name. Hi, my name is ? and I'm a crystal meth addict, he'd said. "You're very well spoken," she added.

"But I hate your parents."

"Oh," Red Streaks said, looking embarrassed and sad. "They did the best they could."

"Bull shit," Sandra said.

"I've forgiven them."

"I haven't," Sandra said, crunching on a stale oatmeal cookie left over from a previous meeting. Of course, if he'd truly forgiven his parents, why had he thrown them under the bus in his share? Addicts – they didn't know what the fuck they really felt, about anything. Still, there was something about him she liked. An intelligence tempered by sweetness. And yes, he was handsome. So kill me, I like handsome men. Most of the men Sandra's age looked like they'd been beaten up by street thugs.

"I'm writing a book about bad parents in literature," she told Red Streaks, "it's called The Evil That They Do. I've already finished the chapters about King Lear's treatment of his children and the feud between the Montagues and Capulets that drove Romeo and Juliet to suicide."

He gazed steadily at Sandra with his wounded, importunate eyes and extended his hand. "My name is Billy."

Billy didn't show up at the next two meetings, which left Sandra more disappointed than she could justify. Even though he was gay, she had worn make-up, blown dry her shoulder-length salt and pepper hair, and dressed up in houndstooth trousers and an Erin Fetherston floral blouse in anticipation of seeing him again. It was silly, she knew, but she couldn't help herself. It was exhilarating to have someone to dress up for. Despite her diatribes against her aging self, Sandra was still compact and slender, with ropy arm muscles that she liked showing off by wearing sleeveless blouses. She had been determined never to have that ugly loose drape that fluttered like signal flags beneath older women's arms. There was an inspirational picture of Michelle Obama ripped from Vogue on Sandra's refrigerator, her bare arms as smooth and hard as mahogany. But Sandra's arms were pale white and a little wrinkled, with pigment spots too large to be freckles. And for the last decade she'd needed skin tight sports bras to keep her breasts aloft. Bette Davis had said it best – getting old ain't for sissies.

After Billy's third no-show, Sandra was determined to stop looking around for him, focusing instead on the book she'd brought with her, Jesus' Son by Denis

Johnson. Gwen had lent it to her as an antidote to the Nazi atrocity tomes Sandra was devouring, books her ex-husband Larry had left behind -- Shirer's The Rise and Fall of the Third Reich, Arendt's The Banality of Evil, McGilbert's Auschwitz and the Holocaust Stories, among others. Larry had been obsessed with the naivete of the Jews, "his people," their willingness to embrace the delusion that Hitler would not pursue mass annihilation. He'd told Sandra about "the road to heaven," a name given by the Nazis at Treblinka to a stretch of pavement bordered by lush trees and fragrant flowers that thousands of desperate souls had mistaken for the path to salvation rather than a noxious death in the gas chambers.

"They went like sheep to the slaughter, no doubt admiring the foliage," Larry said bitterly.

"Maybe delusion was their only option. Maybe they needed it," Sandra had argued.

"The meek will inherit the dirt," Larry said.

"Hi, Sandra," Billy whispered, startling her.

He sat down next to her and withdrew an enormous bottle of cherry-colored sports drink from his backpack.

"Hi, Billy," she said, putting her book down and trying to appear calm even though she felt a little shudder of excitement.

Can she bake a cherry pie, Billy-boy, Billy-boy, can she bake a cherry pie, charming Billy.

My God, what was he stirring up in her?

She recalled with embarrassment a brief affair she'd had in her late twenties with an 18-year-old student in her Shakespeare survey course, a boy who looked like Al Pacino when he was the gorgeous Michael Corleone in The Godfather. The relationship, if you could call it that, had devolved into absurd debates about America's self-image of benevolence and the boy's litany of complaints about the soullessness of his rich parents, although he remained an eager beneficiary of their generosity.

Ridiculous.

"I know that book," Billy said, tapping his finger on the cover of Jesus' Son. "Fuckhead and his burn-out friends, right?"

Oh, God, he was literate.

As soon as the meeting began, Billy raised his hand to share and recounted his latest setback. He'd found a pleasant place he could afford after being evicted from a Board and Care, but when he went to pay the first month's rent, the fellow had already let the place to someone else. So then Billy had nowhere to go.

"I took the only thing I could find, a small room with no windows and a shared bathroom for a hundred dollars more than the other place. It's on San Julian in the flower district, which puts me right in the center of Junkie Town and leaves me flat broke until the beginning of May. So -- what do you think I did?"

Everyone laughed. They all knew what druggies did in the face of adversity.

"I have no luck, you know what I mean? Everything I touch turns to shit."

Ah, yes, self-pity, Sandra thought. It was the infamous addict two-step: Poor me, step forward, I couldn't help it, step back.

After the meeting ended, Sandra volunteered to take Billy downtown in her old BMW sedan, using surface streets rather than the freeway because she had cataracts and didn't like driving fast in the dark. But even though she was happy to have him next to her in the car, she was worried he would spoil it by hitting her up for money.

"Can't your parents at least give you a fifty dollar Ralph's card so you can buy food?" she asked, rolling down her window to inhale the spring air, which smelled like evening primrose.

"Maybe when I see them next week. It's my dad's sixty-fifth birthday," Billy said.

"What will you do in the meantime?" she asked, hoping he had a strategy.

"Starve, I guess."

That was the answer she had anticipated. He's a hustler, she told herself sternly, but her longing for the connection overruled her reason.

"Well, you can come over to my house this weekend and I'll cook dinner for you," Sandra said.

"That would be great." He grinned at her like a boy unwrapping his first Tonka truck. "How about Sunday?"

Billy had said he wanted to cook with her when he came over, and so Sandra had dutifully purchased the ingredients he'd requested: two bunches of fresh spinach, chicken breasts (when had they become so expensive?) and "whatever other salad things you like." Sandra had bought olives, hearts of palm, red and yellow peppers, feta cheese, chopped onions and a jar of artichoke hearts. And then, on impulse, she grabbed a small rib eye roast because she was certain he needed the protein.

The way to a man's heart, a voice in her head sang. Oh, give me a fucking break.

Billy arrived for the dinner nearly two hours late. Sandra had assumed he wasn't coming and she was hurt and furious until she set eyes on him. He looked like he'd just gone two rounds with Oscar de la Hoya.

"I'm so sorry," he said.

"Oh, my God, what happened?"

"I was mugged waiting at the bus stop. I was calling you to say I was on my way when this punk came up behind me and tried to steal my iphone." His parka was ripped and bloodstained and his cheek was badly bruised.

"Oh, no," Sandra said, opening the screen door for him to come inside.

"My parents gave it to me for Christmas so I wasn't about to let some junkie pawn it for drugs."

"Are you hurt? Do you want me to drive you to Emergency?"

"Naw, I'm okay. Really. It looks worse than it is."

"I started cooking without you," Sandra said. "I thought you'd stood me up."

"I'd never do that," he said, looking around the living room, which was lined on three sides with books, the fourth side reserved for her 52-inch flat screen and her collection of DVD's.

"Hope you like roast beef."

"Love it. I'm so sorry to be late," he said. "Can I use your restroom to clean myself up?"

Sandra took note of the word "restroom," which she thought signaled a lengthy bout of homelessness. She also felt a twinge of concern about the contents of her medicine cabinet. There were a few out-of-date Vicodin, left over from the time she'd broken a toe at the gym, and a bottle of powdery Valium she hadn't used since she got sober. To an addict, though, any drug was fair game.

"You've got two bedrooms," Billy said when he came back from the bathroom.

"Oh, yes, the junk room," Sandra said with a nervous laugh because the door to that room was always closed.

"I peeked," Billy said, sensing that he might have overstepped.

"No problem," Sandra said, but his liberty made her uneasy.

They ate dinner in the living room, sitting together on a plush beige sofa watching Robert Downey's Sherlock Holmes: A Game of Shadows.

"This is a very homoerotic film," Sandra commented after some frisky physical business between Watson and Holmes which she hadn't taken note of before.

"It's kind of assumed that they were a gay couple," Billy said, eating hungrily but with careful table manners.

"I didn't know that," Sandra said, recalling the earlier Basil Rathbone versions with the blustering old dimwit of a Watson played by Nigel Bruce. "But I guess that makes sense." Being with Billy reminded her of evenings with Larry. After a decade, they had run out of love for each other but never conversation.

Between dinner and dessert, Sandra and Billy strolled out into the backyard, which was Sandra's favorite part of the property, a small, tree-shaded West Hollywood bungalow she and Larry had purchased in the early 1990's. It was fragrant with herbs and night blooming jasmine, and quiet except for the plinking sounds of water drops in a little faux-stone fountain. Billy surprised her by knowing the names of most of the flowers Sandra had planted, names she had forgotten as soon as the plastic pots they came in were discarded.

"Gardenias," he said, pointing to an array of heady white blossoms in a long, rectangular planter.

"How do you know that?" she asked, impressed.

"Well, the Army moved us around every few years so I learned a lot about what people planted, you know, in the different locations. When I was nine, our neighbor on the left was a real gardenia freak, and that's a scent you never forget." He plucked a flower, held it up to his nose and inhaled deeply. "So how about you?"

"How about me what?"

"I don't know much about you."

"What do you want to know?"

"What were your parents like?"

"Well – my mother was very social, so she was always trying to coax me out of my room, and could never understand why I enjoyed playing by myself and reading books all the time."

"I was the same way when I was a kid. I loved books."

"My father was an intellectual and I worshipped him when I was little but he hated it when I developed ideas of my own and didn't always agree with him. I was more like my father than my mother, but eventually I wasn't like either of them, and for a long time I felt guilty, like I'd disappointed them by being myself."

"I know how that feels."

"Yes, I know you do. But lately, I've been realizing all the good things they did for me and how lucky I've been, compared to a lot of other people. So now I'm more grateful than angry."

"That's good."

"Okay, back to you," Sandra said. "How formally educated are you? Because I think you could be any number of things -- salesman, teacher, actor. You'd be a hell of a drug counselor, if you can stay sober."

"I've only got a GED," he said.

"I don't believe it. You're so bright."

Billy shrugged, smiling apologetically, and handed her the gardenia. It reminded her of the wrist corsage a high school boy had given her before they went off to a dance.

He strolled over to the fountain and reached into the water, pulling up the pump and clearing a clod of black muck from it with his index finger. When he replaced it, the fountain's water output tripled, the staccato plinks transforming into a sustained pebbly ripple.

"You're my hero," Sandra said, feeling a rush of admiration for this man who knew things, knew about flowers and fountains and even Denis Johnson.

"Just hit it with the hose once a week," he said, his cheeks blushing pink.

They went over and sat down on a wooden bench beneath a crepe myrtle tree.

"What did you want to be when – before all this happened?" Sandra asked, mounting her campaign to "save" him.

"I wrote music. I even formed a band when I was in my twenties. I had a synthesizer, a drum machine, a first-rate tape recorder, speakers, a nice little studio set-up. Then I made the biggest mistake of my life and that was the end of that."

"What did you do, for heaven's sake?"

"Ten years in prison on a felony conviction for drug smuggling."

"Jesus, Billy."

Oh, where have you been, Billy-boy, Billy --

"Yeah, I know," he said, smiling ruefully. Sandra noticed for the first time that a couple of his side teeth were missing.

Billy helped Sandra bring the dinner dishes into the kitchen and while she washed them, he returned to the living room and perused the Verizon brochure on her coffee table. It offered a free upgrade to a smartphone if she'd sign up for a new two-year contract.

"This is no good," he said when Sandra emerged from the kitchen with a decanter of coffee, "unless you have money to waste."

"Believe me, I don't."

It was the sort of thing that Larry would have said because, unlike Sandra, who couldn't be bothered, he paid obsessive attention to detail.

"I'll go with you to Metro PCS if you want and help you find the best deal. You can get a smart phone for a lot less than this."

"Oh, that would be great," Sandra said, suddenly thinking of all the other things she needed help with, like changing the recessed light bulbs in the kitchen ceiling, none of which she could reach even with a ladder. She also wanted to redo the grout around the kitchen sink, and replaster the crumbling walls in the laundry room. For a few crazy seconds, she imagined Billy moving into the cluttered second bedroom that had been Larry's home office for his software design business. At least it had windows, unlike his present living arrangement. And it wouldn't take too long to clear it out. Larry's antiquated dot matrix printer, the obsolete desktop computers, how-to books, Nazi books, old clothes and every test he'd ever taken since the first grade. Someday I'll come by and haul it all away, he had promised. But he never got around to it.

Sandra drove Billy home that night without mentioning the spare room, but she couldn't quiet the chatter in her head, the 'helpless female' part of her that wanted a companion, a protector, a handsome man who could fix things – like John Wayne, as Joan Didion had once observed about herself.

"I don't know nothin' about birthin' babies, Missy Scarlet," Larry had said, taunting Sandra for not remembering the directions to his mother's house after a decade of driving there. "I don't need to remember. I have you," she'd protested, but he resented her dependency. "What happened to that fierce warrior I married?" he demanded whenever she felt daunted. "The one who opened her own doors, paid her own way, and challenged the snobby Department Chair for refusing to let screenplays be taught as literature?" (What had Shakespeare written if not scripts, she had argued.)

"She got tired, Larry," Sandra would answer. Can't your fierce warrior ever get tired?

"See that building?" Billy asked, pointing to an expensive looking, renovated apartment complex on the edge of downtown. "That's where my former boyfriend lives."

"Why former?" Sandra asked, picturing the ex as an older, well-to-do father figure.

"I don't know. I guess he got sick of me always fucking things up," Billy said.

The following Tuesday, Billy accompanied Sandra to a Metro PCS store on

Olympic in Korea Town and helped her pick out a free LG Android phone with a $62 a month, 2-year contract. Afterward, he showed her how to use the phone's camera and she snapped two pictures of him, posed handsomely outside the store, before she took him home with her for dinner.

This time Sandra made spaghetti and meatballs, which was quick and good and would be easy to pack up as a leftover for Billy when she drove him home. She wanted him to watch one of her favorite films over dinner, LA Confidential, and set him to work searching for it among her DVD's while she finished cooking.

When she came back into the living room with the salad ten minutes later, Billy looked startled.

"I couldn't find it," he said, quickly going back to the sofa and sitting down.

"That's okay," Sandra said, puzzled by his agitation. She set down the salad bowl and served him a large portion. Then she went over to the shelves of DVD's, which Larry had carefully alphabetized, and spotted it quickly.

"Ta-dah!" she announced, setting it up in the player.

After they'd finished their salads, Sandra took the bowls and brought them into the kitchen, returning with two plates of spaghetti and meatballs and a dish of grated parmesan.

"This movie is so stylized," Billy commented as he sprinkled cheese on the pasta. "It seems old fashioned to me."

Sandra was stricken by his reaction, having expected that he'd love it as much as she did.

"It's deliberately stylized, like a 1940's crime novel," she explained. "Like Dashiell Hammett and Raymond Chandler."

"Uh-huh," Billy said, trying to be agreeable. Sandra picked up the remote and pushed stop.

"We can watch something else if you want," she said.

"No, no," Billy said, "it was fine."

He fell asleep halfway through the musical Chicago, which he'd wanted to see, after finishing off two molten chocolate lava cakes that Sandra had served for dessert. Sandra sat next to him on the sofa, her head starting to ache. The whole evening had seemed different from their first dinner together, more tense and less congenial. She went over to her purse, which she'd left next to the sofa, and took out a bottle of Tylenol. It was a "legal" drug for headaches, even by the strictest NA standards, but she still felt a little guilty when she used it, that slippery slope winking at her devilishly.

Billy woke up when the movie ended, yawned, and requested a large grocery bag for his leftovers, but he fell asleep again on the drive downtown, snoring gently. When they were a few blocks from his apartment, he awakened suddenly and said, "Can you let me off at that little bodega so I can get a few groceries?"

"Did your dad finally give you some money?"

"Oh--no, not yet," he said, "but I'll be okay." He got out of the car, smiling at her with his customary warmth. "Do you remember your way back to the freeway?"

She nodded.

"Roll up your window now," he said, "and lock your door."

She headed north toward Fifth Street, feeling happy that he was concerned for her safety, but as soon as she left downtown, an uneasy gnawing prompted her to fish for her wallet.

Unable to find it without looking, she pulled over, parked, and turned on the overhead light. There should have been $175 in cash from her pension check, three twenties, a ten, one five and a hundred dollar bill; however, they were mixed in with check deposit slips, store coupons for salad dressing and yogurt, torn pieces of paper with various phone numbers, including Billy's, and a ragged prescription for Xanax which she'd never filled. She counted the bills. All the smaller ones were there, but she couldn't find the hundred. She counted again with the same result. Then she pulled everything out of her purse, wallet, Kleenex, Tylenol, hair brush, dental floss, make-up pouch, and the three books she was reading. Nada.

When she got home, she took apart the purse again, laying each item out on the coffee table. The hundred was still missing. She spotted Billy's number on the table and wanted to call him, but how could she be sure? Instead, she got up and searched the sofa, looking to see if the money had fallen onto the floor or been caught between the cushions. Then she wrote down everywhere she had been after she withdrew the cash from the bank the day before. Gas station? She'd used her debit card. Vons? Debit card. The only other place she'd gone was the Metro PCS store with Billy, and she'd paid the tax on the phone with a check. The cash in her wallet had never been touched.

She grabbed her old phone and called Billy.

"Hi," he said, sounding a little surprised. "Did you get home all right?"

"I did," Sandra said quietly.

"How's your new phone working?"

"It's charging. Billy, did you – borrow a hundred dollars from my purse?" She couldn't bring herself to say steal; what if she was wrong?

Billy was silent for a few seconds. "Nooooo," he said finally, drawing out the o's and putting a question mark at the end, like "really?"

"Okay," Sandra said, feeling ashamed. "I'll take another look through my purse, but I know I had it and now it's gone."

"I'm so sorry," Billy said, sounding sincere. "I hope you find it."

"Yeah, thanks," she said. "I can't afford to lose a hundred bucks."

The money didn't turn up. Neither did Billy, at any of the meetings the following week. His disappearance convinced Sandra that he had taken the money and was avoiding her. That must be how he handled things, she reasoned, spoiling relationships like he'd done with his ex-boyfriend and maybe with his parents as well, and then running away and starting over again with someone new.

Sandra felt robbed, not so much of the money as of her trust. She also felt foolish and ashamed of her gullibility, and that made her angry. How dare he steal from her when she had befriended him, fed him, packed up leftovers for him, and driven him all the way home three times despite the ridiculous price of gas. She had even considered letting him move into her house!

That night she couldn't sleep, tossing fitfully, struggling with resentment and an eruption of anxiety she hadn't felt since the divorce. The theft, she realized, had jolted her illusion of safety, leaving her feeling naked and violated in her own home. She pictured the Vicodin in the medicine cabinet with a familiar ache. Maybe just one, one or two, just for tonight so she could sleep. She clutched her belly with both hands and rocked like a distraught infant. Finally she went into the bathroom and opened the medicine cabinet. The Vicodin was gone. So was the Valium.

Three weeks later, when Sandra had finally reconciled herself to never seeing Billy again, he reappeared at a meeting, looking gaunt and anxious. When he smiled at her, she smiled back reflexively but then felt manipulated and quickly looked away. He should have had horns, she thought angrily, and cloven hooves.

Billy shared in the meeting that he'd had another meth relapse and become too depressed to emerge from his room except for more drugs. Sandra looked over at Gwen, shook her head and sighed.

Gwen's eyes narrowed a little and Sandra imagined her saying, "Now, don't get sucked in again, Sandy girl."

Sympathy for the Devil, Sandra mused. The Stones really knew their audience.

She and Gwen were on their way out of the meeting when Billy caught up with them.

"Can I talk to you in private?" he asked Sandra.

Sandra looked at Gwen as if for permission. Gwen shrugged, but her eyes flashed with anger.

"I'll call you later," she said, apologetically, but Gwen did not acknowledge that she'd heard.

Sandra and Billy walked back into the meeting room, by now almost empty except for two people clearing the coffee cups and reboxing the leftover cookies. They went and sat down in a corner.

"You know what I did," Billy said quietly, his eyes wider open than usual.

"Yes," Sandra answered, waiting.

"I'm so ashamed," Billy said. "I know I blew it," he added.

"Yes, you did."

Billy reached into the pocket of his tight maroon jeans and pulled out a hundred dollar bill, folded like origami into a tiny square.

He handed it over to her and repeated, "I'm so sorry," looking as contrite as a little boy who'd been caught stealing quarters from his mother's purse.

"How did you get this?" Sandra asked.

"It doesn't matter."

"Did you steal it from somebody? I want to know."

"I sold my iphone."

"But you loved that phone," Sandra said, feeling guilty despite herself.

"I've got a throw-away one now. I'll give you the number."

"Oh, Billy," Sandra said, shaking her head.

"Will you forgive me?"

"Yes," Sandra said, but as soon as the word came out of her mouth, she realized it was a lie. Something had hardened inside her, like those people with scleroderma whose bodies turn to stone.

It would have been so much easier if Billy hadn't done the right thing. If only he hadn't handed her that hundred dollar bill, hadn't acknowledged that he'd stolen it and said he was ashamed, hadn't come back into her life again.

"I told myself, here is someone I really like," he said as he was walking her to her car. "Sandra and I could actually be friends. And then I blew it all to hell."

"Yes, you did."

She sensed him hesitating for a moment to see if she would offer him a ride home. The impulse arose in her like a wave of nausea, but she sucked in a breath and sighed.

"Goodnight," she said at the same time that he said, "See you."

He walked off down the street in a slow lope, his head down and his arms flat against his sides, moving through the bright circle of a street lamp before disappearing into the shadows.

Later that night, Sandra told Gwen that she felt like one of those abused wives on Dr. Phil who take back their repentant husbands again and again, their puffy, girlish faces stained with black Maybelline tears.

"'He said he'd never do it again,' they whimper, 'and I believed him because I luuuuuuuuuuuuuhhve him.'"

"He's Billy the Kid, Sandy," Gwen said wearily. "He's a drug smuggler and a con and you're a mark."

"I know," Sandra said, "believe me."

"Just remember that you would have taken the Vicodin and broken a sixteen-month sobriety if he hadn't stolen it."

"I guess I owe him then," Sandra said, unable to resist the joke.

"Go fuck yourself."

Fool, Sandra whispered to herself as she lay beneath the quilt in the dark bedroom, exhausted but too agitated to fall asleep. She turned on the television to distract herself. Rachel, Rachel, an old Joanne Woodward film about a jilted schoolteacher, was playing, which quickly drove her thoughts back to Billy. He would want to come visit, have dinner and watch movies with her again, like nothing bad had happened. She vowed not to weaken or relent, but what if he behaved himself, what if he'd learned his lesson? And what if her loneliness overwhelmed her resolve?

Billy called Sandra twice during the next month, the second time from a hospital, and left messages, but she did not return the calls. A week later, he turned up on her doorstep while she was watching Project Runway. It had been an unusually warm evening, and she'd left the front door open to get some night air. Only the screen door stood between them, and he could see her sitting on the sofa, so she couldn't pretend that she wasn't at home.

"Please, Sandy, I need to talk to you. Will you let me come in for a few minutes?"

So now she was Sandy. His voice sounded raw and edgy, which made her uneasy.

"What are you doing here?" she said, getting up from the couch but staying back from the door. "You can't just show up like this, Billy," she said, angry at him for putting her on the spot. "It isn't fair."

"I had to come. I've got nowhere else to turn, Sandy. Please let me in."

"I can't."

"Why not?"

Why not?! "Please leave me alone. Please -- go away. I can't help you, Billy."

He started to cry, a series of throat-clenching, saliva-choked sobs. In the porch light, she could see that his face was dirty and his hair was greasy and uncombed, like the people who roamed the streets with shopping carts full of detritus. And there was that smell -- soiled clothes, dried sweat, something even worse. He must have become homeless again.

"Please let me come in," he said. "I'm begging you."

"Stop it! Call your parents. Call your sponsor. Call your ex-lover, for God's sake," she said, on the verge of tears.

"Let me tell you what happened."

"I don't want to know what happened," she shouted. "I can't save you, Billy."

"You don't understand," he said, clawing at the screen with ragged fingernails.

"Okay, okay," she said, going over to her purse. "I'll give you some money." She was willing to hand over whatever she had, anything to make him go away, even though she knew it was like feeding squirrels.

"Nooo," he said, sounding hurt that she thought he'd come for money. "I just need to talk to you."

"I can't, Billy. I can't do this." Looking down so she wouldn't have to see his face, she pushed the front door closed, turning the lock and fastening the chain.

He began to howl like a crazy person. He was a crazy person, something she should have known from the outset.

She turned off the porch light, the television, and all the lights in the living room and fled to the back of the house, slamming shut the sliding glass door to the backyard, and retreating to the spare room, her whole body shaking.

Here she was, hiding out among the litter of her life with Larry, a life she had longed to move on from. But she'd lost her way, turned to drugs and alcohol, and finally, to delusion. What a pathetic fantasy, that a gay man, a sociopath hopelessly addicted to drugs, might become the beloved companion of her old age.

"We had fed the heart on fantasies. The heart's grown brutal from the fare," Larry recited, poking her in the arm with his imaginary hand. Sandra was surprised to hear Larry quoting Yeats. Poetry had never been his bailiwick.

Jesus Christ! She must be putting Yeats into Larry's mouth, she realized. The preposterousness of it made her laugh out loud.

What the hell was she doing, cowering in the dark like a child afraid of the bogeyman? What was she afraid of? Only herself, really, and that spell was surely broken now.

Okay, okay, you've made your point, you needling asshole, she said, her old affection for Larry's gruff exhortations revived.

She wasn't a child and she wasn't an old woman, either, not yet, and not ever if she had anything to say about it. Whatever came, she would deal with it. Because living required, no demanded, courage. And there was the book, The Evil That They Do, to be written, its message about the consequences of faulty parenting more relevant than ever now, given the plague of feckless millennials texting and sexting their grandiose despair. Yes, there was still important work to be done and the prospect filled her with excitement.

Sandra stood up as gracefully as she could manage from the chaotic clutter of the floor and smacked the dust off her trousers with her palm.

Billy had managed to prop himself up against a large pot of geraniums by the time Sandra came out onto the front porch. He was smoking a cigarette.

She sat down on the steps, not too close, although the Marlboro was masking most of the bad smell. She had left her pocketbook inside but brought her phone, because it was clear that calls would need to be made.

"Okay, Billy," she said in a calm, professional voice, the voice she would have used with a student who had come, however fruitlessly, to dispute a poor grade. "Talk."

Tribe

Barrington Smith-Seetachitt

In the pink light of early morning, the tribe moves across the desert in a loose phalanx, roughly a dozen people across and double that front to back. Their feet sink and slip in the sand, dislodging grains, leaving divots in their wake. Their steps combined create a choir of gentle crunching. The tribe members who walk at the front set the pace, while those with outside positions watch the horizon for greenery, structures, or cloud formations. Today these watchers have the help of a hundred eyes because no one can resist scanning for the scouts who set out—two pairs in opposite directions—in search of water six days ago and have now been gone three days longer than expected.

The tribe's dwindling water supply and the scouts' continued absence has put nerves on edge. Beth—a sun-reddened white woman who walks toward the middle of the group next to a tall, black man named Alvin—is not immune, but resolves to push down her anxiety since it doesn't change the fact that the only thing to do is keep putting one foot in front of the other. (An *excellent compartmentalizer*, her ex-husband Jerry used to call her, in either an admiring or accusing tone, depending on the circumstance.) She concentrates instead on the pleasantness of the morning—the slight breeze, the temperature that is warm but not yet hot, her body in motion, the night's stiffness evaporating. And Alvin. For the past several weeks, or maybe longer, he has walked the day's' first miles with Beth, and she enjoys his company. She likes his matter-of-factness, his ability to be amused by small things and how he doesn't dig for personal revelations beyond her level of comfort.

Beth and Alvin have fallen into the habit of reporting their dreams from the night before, although they seldom remember them completely. Today Alvin recalls only the image of a *ghazal*—a slender-horned gazelle like those from his childhood. Their creamy-buff coats had reflected the sun's rays, he tells Beth, and their enlarged hooves helped them traverse the sands of the Saharan desert. The gazelles were able, he says, to survive merely on the water content from plants and dew from leaves.

"They would eat at night time, mostly, when it was cooler. Once, when I was little-little, my father woke me from my sleep and carried me out to watch a whole herd of them eating near our home. Their furs were glowing in the moonlight."

"That sounds beautiful."

"Yes. It was. I felt...wonder. That is what I felt last night, as well. In the dream."

They fall silent, in deference to feelings of wonder and ruminations about how much simpler life would be if they could survive on the morning's dew.

Beth takes three steps for Alvin's two. While everyone has their own stride, the tribe as a whole has a developed a pace so deliberate that Beth can measure a conversational pause in distance as well as seconds. The tribe's scouts use this predictability as well. They are experts at triangulating the distance the tribe covers in a certain amount of time and plotting a course to intercept, which is why their failure to appear is both uncommon and concerning.

She catches her thoughts drifting, and pushes them back to their prescribed path.

"I dreamed I was late for work." She delivers this as a dry punch line for Alvin.

Not only do her words highlight the difference between their former lives, but the very phrase *late for work* is amusing, an outdated relic of a worry.

She doesn't tell him she'd woken panicked, with a pounding heart. The dream had faded so fast that she was unable to recall what, beyond being late for work, could have evoked such a reaction. The tingle of adrenaline coursing from her heart through her limbs lingers even now, as she keeps her tone light, ready to let the telling rob the dream of its power.

"I was home, but I must have been traveling, because everything was disorganized. My toothbrush was in my travel kit but I couldn't find the toothpaste. Every pair of tights I put on had a hole. I kept frantically opening drawers and feeling under cushions for change for the bus, but I kept coming up short. It was intense. Super-Real."

Super-real. She tries to think how long she's been using that phrase. In the city, the onus had been on immigrants to mimic mainstream English, but here, although English is the common tongue, its native speakers are the minority. Beth isn't the only one who has begun to slip into singsong tones, to omit words that no longer seem necessary, succumbing to the pleasures of new linguistic rhythms. Perhaps in a generation the tribe will have a patois all its own. When they'd first set out, Beth hadn't even considered another generation, but there are four children now. She finds the two youngest riding their parents' shoulders, shaded by umbrellas held in dark mahogany hands. Beth's own hands are chapped and pink despite the gauzy wrappings meant to protect them from the sun.

Hand. Younger, with smooth, unburned skin. Layer of polish on each fingernail. Swish of a paisley-print sleeve at the wrist. Tap of I.D. to sensor on a turnstile.

"And then somehow, I guess I got to the office. I was wearing this shirt, I'd wear when I was in a hurry because it didn't need to be ironed—but after a couple hours it would feel scratchy, and you could never really get the sweat smell out of the armpits. It had too much polyester, or nylon or something."

"Yes! My sister buy clothes at Five-Ninety-Nine on Pico Boulevard. Everything cost $5.99. But the materials are not good—not breathable, you know?" Beth likes the way his accent elongates and inflates the word—Breeeath-ah-ble.

He falls silent. The indistinct chatter of others floats in the air around them, a word surfacing here or there in a mostly murmurous sea. From the far-away look on Alvin's face, Beth knows he is thinking of his younger half-sister, Yaya. As a born citizen, Yaya had had the option to stay in the city when the gates closed, and because she carried a child in her belly she'd done so. She'd wanted to have doctors when the baby came, and she was young—only twenty-four, with twenty-six long years to live. Alvin, older, and with only a green card, had not had the same choice.

In the first days after the announcement, people spoke of going with older relatives, of striking out into the wilderness. But since the storms, even the wilderness was not what it had been, and in the end, almost everyone younger than forty chose to stay in the city. It was the right decision for her, Alvin says when he is feeling doubt. Beth always agrees, partly because it's probably true—and mostly because it's not something that can be changed.

"The city will honor the pact." Alvin says now, wanting to feel convinced.

"They will." She knows the politicians won't deliver on every promise—when did they ever?—but the guaranteed lifespans were the glue holding the whole city together. "They couldn't go back on it. There would be an uproar."

He nods and says nothing for a quarter of a mile. Then, "I had an older sister, you know?"

Beth shakes her head. It is only recently that Alvin has spoken to her of his childhood.

"She wore bright colors. Cottons. When I was three or four, I would watch her jumping a rope with her friends. She could jump so high from the ground." He smiles at the memory, then darkens. "They killed her. They came and burned our village and took my father as well. We called them devils, but it was the government who sent them. Our own government lied to us. When first we arrived in America, my mother—she told me that such things could never happen here. But that was before the storms, you know?"

He lapses into his own thoughts. The day is growing warmer. Walking east, the front of Beth's body heats up first. The skin of her thighs makes contact with the sun-heated fabric of her loose trousers with every forward step.

"But for sure you are right," Alvin says to Beth. "They will keep the pact."

By mid-day, the rocks and scrub look bleached under a sky of hard, unvaried blue. The tribe erects shade sails and gathers underneath them to wait out the hours when the air ripples with heat. Beth has friends with whom she normally shares her meals, but today she finds she is not up to joining a group. Any conversation is likely to turn to speculation about the scouts, which will be both useless and upsetting, and today, for whatever reason, she feels particularly shaky. Still, when Alvin comes to join her in the isolated spot she has chosen near the edge of the largest sail, she feels a flush of happiness she can't deny. Their recent, tentative alliance is something she's avoided pondering. Just because they've enjoyed a stretch of days in each other's' company is no mandate to go labeling things. Lately, though, there's been a question hanging in the air between them before they retreat to their respective tents, a question that has begun to linger, even after she is curled up in her bag, waiting for sleep.

The question is not hers alone. Even in this moment, several tribe-mates cast sliding, casual glances in their direction. Beth imagines the picture she and Alvin make, small and tall, silhouetted against the over-bright landscape. It pains her to be unable to grapple with her feelings unobserved. Of the many luxuries lost in this new life, privacy is one that she misses most.

After a lunch of leathery meat, Beth and Alvin lie on their backs. A couple of flies flit, land, and crawl across their bodies. Beth pats at a tickling rivulet of perspiration between her breasts and encounters the ever-present grittiness of sand against her skin. The scratchy shirt in her dream last night is but one instance of a recurring motif. Scouring pads, crushed apricot-seed face-wash, and coarse-grained laundry detergent poured into gyrating tubs of moving water have all made appearances in her dreams—once common and unquestioned parts of daily life, now tangible only in slumber, dreamlike upon waking.

The sun glares through the thinning canvas shade-cloth. In a sleepy, heat-induced delirium, Beth thinks of laundry, tumbling in a hot dryer. She thinks of chalky perfumed dryer sheets. *April fresh.* She can't summon a memory of the smell. Strange to think there had been so many permutations of clean.

Janitor's cart in the hallway. In her hurry, hip bump, thump. Plastic bottle landing on thin, print carpet, rolling. Pink liquid sloshing inside like a stormy sea.

A smell, like bubble-gum. Or flowers.

"Bubble gum flowers for sure a dream," murmurs Alvin, when she rouses herself enough to report this newly remembered addendum.

"Clean for sure a dream," she says, and her borrowed syntax prompts his barking laugh before they both lapse back into stupor.

A few months ago, two scouts had found an untouched well, a heavy cover bolted over its low, stone wall. It had been pure chance they'd stumbled across it since the adjacent house, collapsed into its basement, was invisible to anyone scanning the horizon from a distance. The tribe members had speculated on who might have lived there as they sifted through the rubble in search of salvageable items. Who would have chosen to live so far from any town? A hermit? An eccentric? Maybe a celebrity tired of public life. Someone who'd had money enough to commission the well—which was almost a thousand feet deep. They had wondered as they washed—bodies and clothes. They had reveled in the strange feeling of clean. They'd camped for weeks, even planted and picked some quick growing lettuce, before being discovered by marauders, who have a knack for finding anything good.

There are a few factions of marauders, often assembled around ex-military personnel whom it's rumored were stationed in the desert and somehow left behind when the cities closed their gates. Marauders have fighters and guns and no children or elderly. The tribe, having children and elderly and no guns, had agreed early on to walk away from conflicts when possible and trust luck they would find what they needed again.

Since walking away from the well, however, water finds have been small, the rains few, and now some are wondering if they might have trusted luck too much.

Left. Left. I left my wife in New Orleans with fifty kids and a can of beans. The sand on the ground is coarser than in the morning and spread more thinly so that it crunches underfoot in time to the childhood chant Beth realizes has been repeating in her head. The second leg of the day's journey is always harder. Everyone is drained by the heat and the first set of miles, though Beth can't help but smile as she tracks Alvin up ahead, moving between people, talking and joking. Another aspect of him she has come to appreciate—his unflagging morale.

Beth has drifted toward the back of the group, letting her mind wander as it will. The chant, upon her awareness, morphs into a song: *Everything you own in a box to the left.* She can't remember any other words, although she recalls it was about a woman kicking her man out of the house for cheating. Despite his transgressions, Beth finds herself feeling sorry for the man, exiled with his meager belongings, unable to ever return home.

The temperature drops as the sun approaches the horizon. Beth feels the relief of it, even knowing it will soon settle into chill. As soon as they stop walking she'll strip off her sweat-dampened clothes and trade them for dry ones before the desert night turns cold. When the tribe was new, made up of strangers sitting around the fire at night, they'd compared cold-night dreams that revealed their lives: over-air-conditioned hotel room, snowy days in Michigan, chilled oceans, swimming pools and walk-in freezers.

Beth had never shared hers: icy chemotherapy dripping through her veins. Especially in the tribe's early days, she had avoided disclosing anything that hinted she might be weak or a burden. Certain codes of conduct had been suggested to the tribes before they'd left the city, but of course there was no oversight. Some people had talked tough in interviews, saying it would be logical to cull the old and weak once they were outside the gates. As it turns out, the group of people Beth was assigned to—her tribe—has always taken care of each other.

But even if she'd known there was no danger in mentioning her history, she wouldn't have wanted people whispering, saying she should have stayed in the city, with its medicines and doctors. She'd heard this enough before she left, from friends, and from Jerry who would rather—

April fresh. April.
The memory arrives with such force that Beth stumbles, catches herself with a heavy footfall.
Rough texture of cubicle walls. Ink marks on the white laminate desk. Soft "gong" of computer booting. Screen flickering to life.

It had not happened at morning, as in the dream, but later, after a long day of off-site meetings. She'd arrived at her desk impatient to answer some emails she knew were

waiting—this was before portable electronics had made everything accessible. The information she needed was still tethered to one machine. When the login screen appeared, it took her a moment to process that the usual desktop image had been replaced. In the new photograph there was Jerry, holding a sign that said, "It's April 8, do you know when your husband's birthday is?"

The remorse she'd felt was sudden and hot. In the photograph on her screen, Jerry had been grinning good-naturedly, no sign of reproach in his eyes. He'd often joked that if a plumber's family was the last to get their pipes fixed, the husband of an event producer was destined to miss a few birthday presents. He'd always been understanding of her calendar filled with an endless parade of deadlines. But seeing the picture, she had known the truth—she was cheating. Not with any person, but in the way she became caught up with her own life and let him disappear. She loved him and yet she could forget about him completely—for hours, even days—when they were apart. She knew that when important moments happened in his life, he thought about her, but she never managed to reliably return the favor.

Even now.

A woman named Myra keeps the official calendar for the tribe. Beth goes through the motions of confirming the date, although she knows, she has known, of course she has known. She returns to the back of the group, treading upon a moving tapestry of long afternoon shadows cast by row after row of her companions. She feels dizzy at the sight. The thought occurs that simply by virtue of being vertical, they are sundials, their shadows marking the turning of the earth, the passing of time. Tempus breve est, her Latin teach had taught them in high school, saying that one day they would understand.

A sense of hysteria comes over her. She opens her mouth, feeling she has to release whatever is inside, unsure if it will be sound or laughter or vomit, but nothing comes out, For a moment it is like a dream where one is frozen, unable to scream. But then she feels the air hitting her wet face and realizes that tears are rolling down her cheeks. Water from her eyes is falling, wasteful, in the sand.

That night, the tribe gathers to officially discuss their situation. Beth is perched on her low canvas stool not too far from the fire when Alvin finds her. He sets his bony frame on a slab of rock, then rises to rotate and adjust it. "What was that word they had for the chairs, with the—?" he mimes adjusting levers.

"Ergonomic?" Beth guesses.

"Yes. My rock for the evening is ergonomic."

He grins at her, firelight reflecting on his skin and teeth. She feels him observing her, knows others have told him about her crying. She dreads answering questions, but he doesn't ask any. Instead he reaches for her hand and clasps it.

For the first time, she does not let go, but holds on tight.

"Our pace has been consistent," says Ernesto at the meeting, his tone defensive because he is one who often walks in front. "It doesn't make sense that both pairs of scouts would overshoot our path."

"Maybe they not find water at first, but see the green and decide to go more far," says Noi, an older Thai woman. "It take longer, but they come."

"Or they *did* find water, but ran into others who didn't feel like sharing." This comment, from their sole Brit, Alistair, prompts a silent moment. There are rumors of communities who have ceased being nomadic, having found sufficient resources to live—at least in limited numbers. With no walls for defense it makes sense they would go to great lengths to protect the secrecy of their locations. If the scouts have encountered one of these communities, they won't be returning.

The main question to address is when the tribe should send out more people, and who should go. The conversation is heated, has disintegrated into hubbub when a voice near Beth says, "If they don't come back by morning, I will go and look."

It takes her a moment to comprehend that it is Alvin's voice she is hearing, that he has volunteered to go. Slowly she unwraps her stiffened fingers and pulls her hand away from his.

As soon as the meeting is over, Beth retreats to her tent. Alvin follows. "I am older. Better to have the young ones here, if there is a fight. And I have known the desert."

"Of course," she says, "that makes sense." She knows he wants her to look up and meet his eyes. She waits out the long moment until he realizes she won't.

"Good night then." His steps make no sound as he walks away.

In her tent, Beth curls against the cold. She wonders about Jerry's death. The government's informational programs had promised "a ritual," but hadn't specified what that meant, emphasizing only that people would have different options to choose from. One late night comedy show became momentarily famous for an inspired, "Poisoned vodka martini, or poisoned cupcake?" sketch. Jerry had signed his contract without knowing any details.

After Beth's cancer diagnosis, even before her treatment was complete, people had begun calling her a survivor. It made her uncomfortable—at times angry. It was ridiculous to have them ascribe to her some heroic quality that made her deserving of survival as she shivered, puked, and languished—completely dependent on the efforts of others.

Jerry had stayed by her side throughout, seeming never to flinch. It wasn't until later, after the storms began, that she learned how those months of watching her suffer had affected him. How, during the worst of it, he had vowed that for himself he would choose quality of life over quantity—if time to choose should ever come.

The time, as it turned out of course, had come for everyone. And only then had Beth realized she had indeed been transformed—not overnight, but so gradually that under different circumstances she might never have noticed—into her own version of a *survivor*. She found she was incapable of accepting that anyone—doctor or government official—should tell her how long she would live. She no longer cared about risks or statistics. She wanted to envision possible futures and embrace them without the limitation of fear. That's what she'd said to Jerry, as they lay in their bed together for the last time: *Without limitation of fear.* Big words to live up to.

The half moon provides some help as Beth carries her bedroll through the icy night, and crouches outside Alvin's tent. He unzips the door for her and pulls her inside without a word. Later, he will curl around her, his body curved like a gazelle's slender horn and she will close her eyes and dream of two figures making their way across the sand.

Turn, Turn, Turn

Thelma Zirkelbach

Turn, Turn, Turn: From a Song by The Byrds Based on The Book of Ecclesiastes

"To everything (turn, turn, turn)
There is a season (turn, turn, turn)"
     The Byrds

My world has been turning for 82 years. My life began in Austin, Texas in 1935. I was a skinny child with long, Shirley Temple curls and was so shy I hid behind my mother's skirt when strangers visited. I was afraid of many things, including putting my face in water in a swimming pool, going to bed in the dark, and fairy tales with wolves. My entire first grade year, I threw up every morning before school, even though once I arrived, I loved being there.

No one would have predicted that eight decades later I'd be a strong, independent woman. I even surprise myself. I have weathered many turning points in my life, some happy, some sad.

Although I wouldn't trade the happy ones, it's the difficult ones that have strengthened me.

"Some women are lost in the fire. Some women are built from it." I don't know who originally said this, but I know it's true—literally. My first turning point in life came on March 29, 1955, two months before my twentieth birthday. What began as a sweet spring day ended with a blustery norther. One of my roommates turned on the gas heater but neglected to shut the window behind it. While I stood chatting with another girl, a gust blew my full-skirted dress into the stove and caught it and me on fire. Burned over 35% of my body. I spent three months in a burn ward at John Sealy Hospital in Galveston. I was a terrible patient. I screamed with pain, frightening other patients and annoying the nurses, who said I was a crybaby. What did they know? They may have treated burns but they'd never experienced the excruciating pain that accompanies them. Afterward, I was left with a fear of fire and scars on my back and legs that would never disappear, but I gained new confidence knowing I had been strong enough to survive and thrive. Ignoring the scars and the bandages I wore to keep my legs from swelling, I returned to college and, honed by fire, went on with my life.

I graduated from the University of Texas in 1957, moved to Houston, married, and had two children. My life was that of a typical suburban housewife—carpools, outings with the children and my husband, dinner parties, the League of Women Voters and other organizations. Then, on August 1, 1966 everything changed. I remember the date vividly because it marked a turning point in my life and also a date that would be long remembered at the University of Texas and in the city of Austin. Just after lunch a friend called. "Someone is shooting people from the UT Tower," she sobbed. I turned on the radio and learned that a deranged student named Charles Whitman had taken the elevator to the observation deck of the iconic UT landmark and was randomly firing a rifle at students crossing the campus mall or walking down Guadalupe Street across from the campus. I was terrified. My sister was in Austin, visiting our parents and I knew she and my mother planned to meet friends for lunch at a restaurant near the campus. Until I learned they were safe, I was a wreck. I called my husband, shakily told him the news, and asked him to come home as soon as he could. "I'm working late tonight," he said casually. "Please don't," I begged. He refused. I lay awake until he strolled in, after midnight. From that day on, he continued to "work late," sometimes wandering in well into the night. I knew he was having an affair, but I endured his nightly outings, his increasing nastiness during the day, and our constant arguments for over a year. I cried myself to sleep, lost weight, and sank into depression, unable to break away from a miserable marriage, unable to brave the 1960's stigma of divorce and its aura of failure. I asked myself if I could manage on my own. For some reason, I constantly worried about what I would do if the car broke down. Finally, after a heated argument, my husband moved out, and the very next day the car broke down. I managed just fine and from then on, freed from despair, I realized I could get along quite well without him.

The following year I met Ralph, and two years later we began a happy marriage. Many years later as we walked across a parking lot on a muggy September night, Ralph remarked, "I think I'm getting a cold." That moment would mark another turning point in my life and Ralph's. The cold lingered with fever, fatigue, and an abnormal blood count. Finally we heard the diagnosis: leukemia. Along with the shock came a queasy feeling. I was writing a book for Harlequin in which the heroine's son had leukemia, and I had the weird sensation that I had caused Ralph's illness by my choice of plot. I knew better, of course, but I agonized over whether he would survive and, if he didn't, if I would survive without him. Our world spun out of control. He endured chemotherapy, a stem cell transplant, pneumonia, and hospital "accidents"—a botched spinal tap that caused paralysis of his legs, a fall onto concrete from a wheelchair that the nurse had neglected to belt him into, inability to swallow that wasn't dealt with for several weeks. Meanwhile, I worked every weekday from 8:00 to 6:30, rushed to the hospital to eat some semblance of dinner and spend the night in his room, get up at 6:00, race home to feed the cats and then back to work another day. That same year, my mother died and my son had a heart attack. And then, the worst news: the leukemia had resurfaced and Ralph was too weak for another transplant or even a round of chemo. Seven weeks after that grim announcement, on a crisp fall morning, he passed away. Grief-stricken, sobbing, I walked out of the hospital into blinding sunlight that was so at odds with my sorrow. I remember the next months as "the time of tears and fears." But, slowly and unwillingly at first, I learned to live on my own in what widows refer to as "the new normal"

I thought, having experienced the worst year of my life, I could handle anything, but life had another lesson to teach me. On Memorial Day 2015 it rained. Actually, rain had been falling sporadically for a week, soaking the ground. That evening thunder rumbled as I turned off the light and curled up in bed. I heard rain beating against my window but I didn't pay much attention. I drifted off and slept through the night. The next morning I got out of bed . . . and stepped into ankle-deep water. "Oh, my God," I wailed over and over as I waded across the floor and down the hall from room to room. I peered outside. My street looked like a river, with water sloshing into my yard and all my neighbors'. I didn't know what to do. I thought, what would Ralph do? I spent the next hours wandering through my house, assessing the damage—the soaked Oriental rugs, the dishwasher that no longer worked, the water stains on every wall. That afternoon, as the water receded, neighbors congregated outside on sodden yards. Soon our lawns were littered with piles of torn-out carpet, ruined furniture and other debris. Pickup trucks trundled along the street, stopping every now and then so their occupants could scavenge items from people's lawns. During the next days, our neighbors became a community of problem solvers. With their support and that of friends and family, I made my way through the maze of insurance adjustors, FEMA representatives, water damage repair services, and scammers who offered to buy my house, sell my house, and repair my house. Fortunately, I had hired a realtor before the flood because I had made plans to move into a nearby senior residence. Within a month, I sold my house to a builder. When the day came to leave the house where I'd lived with Ralph, raised our children, and made dozens of memories, I walked through each room, whispering goodbye and then I moved on. I'd weathered a literal storm this time, and again, surprised myself with resilience.

I often wonder how much of the curly-headed little girl is left after so many years. Yes, there are bits and pieces. I'm still shy in large groups, still uncertain in new situations, but I'm different in many ways. In 82 years I've grown old in wisdom, but remained young in spirit.

And I hope my world will keep turning for a while longer.

Contributors' Notes

Ruth Boggs is a native of Germany and has earned an M.A. in Professional Writing and Editing from George Mason University. She has traveled the United States extensively in her career as a translator and interpreter. Her professional memoir, if she ever chooses to write it, has the working title *From the Whorehouse to the White House* because she's covered it all in the line of duty! She's been an avid reader since age four. Now semi-retired and active in various writers' groups, she is finally focusing on her true passion, which is writing.

William Cass has had over a hundred short stories appear in a variety of literary magazines and anthologies such as december, Briar Cliff Review, and Ruminate. Recently, he was a finalist in short fiction and novella competitions at Glimmer Train and Black Hill Press, received a Pushcart nomination, and won writing contests at Terrain.org and The Examined Life Journal.

Julie Carrick Dalton has published more than a thousand articles in The Boston Globe, BusinessWeek, The Hollywood Reporter, and other publications. She is a graduate of GrubStreet's Novel Incubator, a year-long, MFA-level novel intensive, and she has a Master's in Creative Writing from Harvard University Extension School. She has published short stories in the Charles River Review and The MacGuffin. Julie is the winner of the 2017 William Faulkner Literary Contest and the 2017 Writer's League of Texas literary and mainstream fiction contest. She contributes regularly to DeadDarlings.com and GrubStreet's writer's blogs. She also owns and operates a 100-acre farm. An active mother of four, she enjoys skiing, kayaking, cooking vegetarian food, and digging in the dirt.

PJ Devlin knew she was a writer from the moment she learned the alphabet and put pencil to paper. She loves entering John Gardner's "fictive dream" where a story leads her beyond her concept, and characters enter uninvited, fully formed and demanding voice. For PJ, stories become reckonings where wonder, folly, love, hate, rage, and regret seep from the subconscious and forge paths to understanding, sometimes even epiphany. As she assumed the responsibilities of adulthood, PJ deferred her dream of writing fiction to commence a thirty-year career with Fairfax County, VA government. Upon retirement, she entered the George Mason University Creative Writing Program. In 2011, she earned an MFA. Now, she writes short stories and historic novels, mostly set in Philadelphia, near the Wissahickon Creek. *Wissahickon Souls* and *Becoming Jonika* are historic novels, and *Wishes, Sins and the Wissahickon Creek* is a short story collection, all of them published by Possibilities Publishing Company. Currently, PJ is at work on a magical realism trilogy set along the Wissahickon Creek.

Wendy Fontaine is a mother, writer and writing instructor in Los Angeles. Her work has appeared in literary magazines such as Hippocampus, River Teeth, Passages North, Tiferet and Lunch Ticket, and various news sites like Huffington Post and Role/Reboot. She is at work on two manuscripts: a memoir and a mystery novel. For more, check out her website at wendyfontaine.com.

Brandon French is the only daughter of an opera singer and a Spanish dancer, born in Chicago at the end of the Second World War. She has been (variously) assistant editor of Modern Teen Magazine, a topless Pink Pussycat cocktail waitress (that's another story!), an assistant professor of English at Yale, a published film scholar, a playwright and screenwriter, director of development at Columbia Pictures Television, an award-winning advertising copywriter and creative director, a psychoanalyst in private practice and a mother. Fifty of her stories have been accepted for publication by literary journals and anthologies, she is a Pushcart nominee and was nominated twice for the Kirkwood Prize in Fiction at UCLA. She was also an award winner in the 2015 Chicago Tribune Nelson Algren Short Story Contest and she has a published collection of poetry entitled "*Pie.*"

Ted Harrison is a former television newsman, who worked as anchor, correspondent and producer specializing in politics and government. Along the way he has also been a bookseller and hotline phone operator. His printed work has been published by Main Street Rag Publishing, Dead Mule School of Southern Literature and Pamlico Writers Group.

Joani Peacock is an Episcopal priest and associate for "Liturgy & Hilarity" at Emmanuel on High in Alexandria, Va. She is also a blogger, storyteller, and mental health evangelist @Unorthodox & Unhinged and @Sex & The Single Vicar. In addition, she is a cheerleader for and veteran of the Story District stage; bibliomaniac volunteer at the Library of Congress; Washington, D.C., born and bred; half-marathoner and avid pedestrian; friend to many and mother of four.

Barrington Smith-Seetachitt lives in Los Angeles where she does typical Los

Angeleno things like write screenplays while working various day jobs and trying to eat less carbs, but she's an Indiana girl at heart. Barrington has an MFA in Creative Writing from Florida State University and an MFA in Screenwriting from University of Southern California. She has published fiction and creative nonfiction in Sycamore Review, Colorado Review, The Drum as well as Devilfish Review -- a free online journal where you can read the first story in the trilogy of which *Tribe* is a part, called *To Fairer Weather*. You can also find her at barringtonsmith.net.

Kelli Sullivan writes from her home in Houston, Texas where she lives with her husband and a rescue poodle named Nancy Drew. She is currently completing a graduate program at Rice University, and will receive her Master's in Liberal Studies in May of 2018. Kelli has worked in hotel management and as a PAC administrator and political liaison for a law firm, raised an only-child, and has owned a garden design business. In the Land of Enchantment began as an assignment for a course she completed last spring, MLSC 631 Introduction to Reading and Writing Fiction. She believes that while change can sometimes be frightening, many of life's turning points are seeded with the most exquisite and unexpected gifts.

Thelma Zirkelbach leads a double life. She's a writer who has published personal essays, poetry, memoir and romantic suspense. She's also a speech-language pathologist who works with young children. She's a native Texan who lives in Houston and shares her home with two tuxedo cats.

Acknowledgements

First and foremost I want to acknowledge, and thank *everyone* who submitted to this anthology. We were overwhelmed with submissions this year, and were faced with some really difficult decisions in narrowing it down to what you see in this book. Having our submission count nearly double from last year was gratifying and inspiring, even as every rejection we sent was a tiny stab to our hearts.

This anthology is structured as a contest, and while I didn't want to structure the book around winners and honorable mentions, I did want to congratulate Joani Peacock for her first place win with *Scarlet Letter, No More,* Wendy Fontaine for her second place win with *Family Recipe,* and Ted Harrison for his third place win with *Quinton Parnell Arrives on Ocracoke.*

I owe a huge thank you (and probably cupcakes) to our judges, Terri J. Huck from Eaton Press and Jessica Piscitelli Robinson, author and founder of Better Said Than Done. These ladies know what a good story is, and they read through all of the stories in a fairly short period of time and provided thoughtful and considered feedback, which was essential in helping me pick the finalists.

I am forever indebted to the people who support me and make up the "we" of Possibilities Publishing Company (in no particular order): Kimberly Schor who has been my anthology coordinator since the beginning. This anthology, (and so many other things) would never get past the idea stage without her attention to detail and dedication to the project; my cover designer Tim Ford who puts up with my impossibly tight deadlines and series of "I forgot to mention" emails and always comes through with beautiful covers; my fantastic intern from George Mason University, Yousra Medhkour, who also put up with tight timelines and provided excelent copy editing and organizational services; Lindsay Barry, who kept other projects on track while my attention was taken up with this anthology; and finally my author and friend PJ Devlin, who said to me four years ago "you should start an annual anthology contest!"

Made in the USA
Columbia, SC
26 November 2017